PSYCHOLOGICAL ASPECTS
OF FACIAL FORM

Proceedings of a sponsored symposium honoring
Professor Robert E. Moyers
Held February 29 and March 1, 1980, in Ann Arbor, Michigan

Edited by
G. WILLIAM LUCKER
KATHERINE A. RIBBENS
JAMES A. McNAMARA, JR.

This volume is supported in part by
USPHS Grants DE03610 and DE05095

Monograph No. 11
Craniofacial Growth Series

Center for Human Growth and Development
The University of Michigan
Ann Arbor, Michigan
1980

SYMPOSIUM PARTICIPANTS

Speakers

ELLEN S. BERSCHEID, Professor of Psychology, University of Minnesota, Minneapolis, Minnesota.

LEE W. GRABER, Associate Professor of Orthodontics, Loyola University School of Dentistry, Chicago, Illinois.

GERALD R. ADAMS, Associate Professor of Family and Human Development, Utah State University, Logan, Utah.

G. WILLIAM LUCKER, Assistant Research Scientist, Center for Human Growth and Development, The University of Michigan, Ann Arbor, Michigan.

IAN R. MUNRO, Assistant Professor of Surgery, University of Toronto, Ontario, Canada.

ANNE REDMOND, Assistant Professor of Psychiatry, University of Maryland School of Medicine, Baltimore, Maryland.

Discussion Leaders and Panelists

JAMES R. HAYWARD, Chairman, Department of Oral Surgery, University of Michigan School of Dentistry, Ann Arbor, Michigan.

LYSLE E. JOHNSTON, Chairman, Department of Orthodontics, St. Louis University, St. Louis, Missouri.

HAZEL J. MARKUS, Assistant Professor of Psychology, Assistant Research Scientist, Institute for Social Research, The University of Michigan, Ann Arbor, Michigan.

M. HASKELL NEWMAN, Assistant Professor of Plastic Surgery, The University of Michigan, Ann Arbor, Michigan.

HOWARD A. SATHER, Associate Professor of Dentistry, Mayo Medical School and University of Minnesota, Rochester, Minnesota.

RONALD P. STRAUSS, Associate Professor of Dental Ecology, University of North Carolina, Chapel Hill, North Carolina.

DONALD M. TILGHMAN, Director of Dentistry and Oral and Maxillofacial Surgery, The Johns Hopkins University School of Medicine, Baltimore, Maryland.

SOLICITED CONTRIBUTORS

ROBERT C. COLLIGAN, Associate Professor of Psychology, Mayo Medical School, Rochester, Minnesota.

LAWRENCE DONNER, Associate Professor of Psychiatry, University of Maryland, Baltimore, Maryland.

MICHAEL C. HOLLEN, Resident in Orthodontics, Mayo Graduate School of Medicine, Rochester, Minnesota.

KATHY KAPP-SIMON, Center for Craniofacial Anomalies and Department of Psychiatry, University of Illinois, Chicago, Illinois.

A. HOWARD SATHER, Associate Professor of Dentistry, Mayo Medical School, Rochester, Maryland.

RONALD P. STRAUSS, Associate Professor of Dentistry, University of North Carolina, Chapel Hill, North Carolina.

DONALD TILGHMAN, Associate Professor and Director, Division of Dentistry and Oral and Maxillofacial Surgery, The Johns Hopkins Medical Institution, Baltimore, Maryland.

TABLE OF CONTENTS

PREFACE

The purpose of the Seventh Annual Symposium on Craniofacial Growth held at The University of Michigan on February 29 and March 1, 1980 was to provide an interdisciplinary setting for discussion of the chosen topic, "Psychological Aspects of Facial Form." Due to this year's subject, the symposium provided an even more unique function than it has in previous years—that of bringing together for the first time distinguished researchers and clinicians from the social sciences and biomedical sciences who are concerned with facial appearance in one way or another. Not only does this volume provide a 'first' for this rather new field, but it does so in a truly interdisciplinary manner since it includes the work of people from such apparently disparate fields as plastic and oral surgery, psychology and psychiatry, and dentistry and orthodontics. By including both the most current theoretical work of researchers and the experience of clinicians who are in a position to make use of the results of the theoretical work, this volume bridges the gap between the social and biological sciences. Finally, and perhaps most importantly, this volume should provide a foundation for further thought and research concerning facial form and physical attractiveness.

The symposium honors Dr. Robert E. Moyers, Fellow of the Center for Human Growth and Development and Professor of Dentistry. Dr. Moyers, one of the leading scientists in the field of craniofacial growth and development, embodies the spirit in which the symposium is held. As the first Director of the Center for Human Growth and Development he was responsible for its development into a world renown center for interdisciplinary research.

The symposium is funded in part through the generosity of Dr. and Mrs. Verne Primack of Saginaw, Michigan, and in part through the sale of the symposium volumes. It is jointly sponsored by the Center for Human Growth and Development and The University of Michigan School of Dentistry.

We would like to acknowledge the assistance of those individuals without whom publication of this volume would not be possible. Dr. Barbara Nesbitt prepared the text using The University of Michigan Textedit Computer Program. Ms. Teryl Lynn Schessler helped with the editing of the volume and redrew many of the figures used in the text. Mr. Steve McKelvy prepared the final computer tapes used for setting the type. We gratefully acknowledge the assistance of each of these individuals.

K. Ribbens
G. W. Lucker
J. A. McNamara, Jr.

AN OVERVIEW OF THE PSYCHOLOGICAL EFFECTS OF PHYSICAL ATTRACTIVENESS

Ellen Berscheid, Ph.D.

Professor of Psychology
University of Minnesota

The title not withstanding, this paper has three aims, only one of which is to provide an overview of the psychological effects of physical attractiveness. The others are to, first, place this volume addressed to the psychological aspect of facial form in rough, historical perspective, and second and most importantly, to discuss the most common reaction people display to their suspicion or discovery of the impact that physical attractiveness has upon an individual's life. With respect to this last aim, it will be argued that our collective reluctance to acknowledge the true impact of physical attractiveness has affected research on this problem in the past and it probably continues to affect research and practice today.

THE STUDY OF THE PSYCHOLOGICAL EFFECTS OF FACIAL APPEARANCE

To begin, the importance of this volume addressed to the "psychological aspects of facial form" should be noted for a number of reasons. Among these is that it brings together, for the first time, a number of different research disciplines, all of which are concerned with facial physical appearance in one way or another, but which are characterized by different perspectives, different concerns, and different methodological and analytical tools as well as different subject populations. To make this volume even more unusual, it includes the work of practitioners who are in a position to make use of the fruits of the researchers' theoretical and empirical efforts. An event which is interdisciplinary and which also bridges both basic and applied interests is rare within any scientific enterprise.

This volume is an especially salutary event for another reason. Although inquiry into the psychological effects of physical appearance has spanned several disciplines (including psychology, psychotherapy, medicine, sociology, dentistry, and so on), researchers within these disciplines generally have not been in close communication with one another. Indeed, not infrequently they have been only dimly aware of each other's existence.

1

There especially has been a lack of communication and collaboration across the two principal clusters of researchers in the area: the social scientists, on the one hand, and, on the other, the clinicians who necessarily become interested in the subject of facial aesthetics (e.g., Peck and Peck, '70) because what they do has the alteration of facial form either as its primary purpose or as its unavoidable by-product. Included in the latter group are plastic surgeons, oral surgeons, and orthodontists, as well as psychiatrists, clinical psychologists, and other psychotherapists who are sometimes involved in assessing the psychological prognosis and results of such alteration procedures.

The different concerns of these two groups has resulted in two distinct bodies of research pertaining to the appearance of the human body, as Kalick, a social psychologist, has outlined. He notes ('78):

> The social scientists have dealt with physical appearance as a feature of the social order, and have tried to determine the social consequences of being relatively attractive or unattractive. The clinicians—primarily psychiatrists and plastic surgeons—have studied the personal adjustment patterns of individuals who seek help because they are unhappy with their body image. Many such people seek to have some feature of their body surgically revised.

The "Clinical" Research Tradition

As Kalick ('77) describes, the philosophy and rationale for performing facial alterations have changed over the years, and with these changes have come some very practical and compelling reasons for clinical practitioners to do research on the mental health of candidates for (and recipients of) facial alteration procedures. Plastic surgery and other alteration procedures were originally (circa the late 1600's) directed largely toward severe bodily disfigurements with the use of such restorative and reparative procedures as were available. The modern clinical practitioner, however, is not only called upon to restore grossly damaged body parts, but is also frequently asked to alter medically normal, but unaesthetic, features to make them more pleasing and attractive to the eye.

This significant change in practice has put the clinician squarely into the arena of making value judgments. Few, for example, would stop to question the performance of facial alteration procedures for a child whose face has been ravaged by a wild animal or for a person whose diseased gums and teeth threaten their survival. The performance of cosmetic (or aesthetic) alteration procedures, on the other hand, does raise questions, and these questions lead as frequently to value judgments for answers as they do to objective facts. Frequently, these value judgments center

2

around the question of whether or not the person who wishes the alteration to be performed will truly benefit from the procedure and will be satisfied with the results.

Estimation of satisfaction with the results became a particularly important spur to clinical research when it became distressingly apparent that some people reacted very badly to the alteration; moreover, they sometimes reacted badly even though (to other eyes) the procedure had achieved acceptable—even laudable—aesthetic results. Although such malcontents were few in number, they caused a great deal of discomfort for the practitioners who were involved with them, and interest in screening out such potential disasters from the population of persons requesting facial alterations developed.

As a consequence, the clinical research tradition has devoted a good deal of effort to uncovering a person's motives for cosmetic surgery and other alteration procedures, to identifying the personality patterns characteristic of those who request surgery, and to relating these to their satisfaction with the alterations after they have been made. An investigation by Baker and Smith ('39) is illustrative. These authors examined the records of 312 patients with facial disfigurements and classified them into three psychological categories: (a) normal, well-adapted personalities; (b) inadequate, recessive personalities; and (c) psychotic and borderline personalities. Baker and Smith stated that plastic surgery was indicated for the normals, that it was definitely not desirable for the psychotic borderline group, and that it was a matter for the surgeon's very cautious decision for inadequate and recessive personalities.

In his review of clinical research efforts, Kalick ('78) contends that Baker and Smith's psychological classification scheme, as well as their advice to practitioners, has been reflected in a good deal of later work within the clinical tradition. He cites as an example an article by Hill and Silver ('50), who maintained that the proportion of normal, well-adapted people among plastic surgery patients was small. These authors further commented that:

> It would not be much of an exaggeration to state categorically that the desire leading to actual consultation of the surgeon should be regarded as a symptom of neurosis . . . This consultation of the surgeon should be sharply differentiated in its significance as a symptom from the mere wish to look better. (Quoted by Kalick, 1978).

There are other examples of the view that a desire for facial alteration is a symptom of neurosis. Indeed, as late as the 1960's, studies conducted to assess the psychological health of plastic surgery patients tended to find that large percentages of them showed abnormal personality configurations. Edgerton and co-workers ('61), for example, classified 16% in their sample as psychotic, 20% as neurotic, and 35% as exhibiting personality trait disorders. That left only about 30% as falling within the latitude of psychological health. Such studies, of course, showed only an association, or correlation, between psychic abnormality and a request for plastic surgery; they did not reveal the causal relationship between the two. Nevertheless, the fact of association tended to be interpreted as suggesting that neurosis causes a dissatisfaction with physical appearance—that neurotics fastened upon their appearance as the cause of all their problems, and thus became candidates for plastic surgery. Naturally, the causal scenario went, an alteration in appearance cannot cure neurosis, and so the dissatisfaction that is simply the symptom of the neurosis must necessarily remain even after the facial alteration is made—and cause problems for the practitioner who performs it.

Oddly enough, this causal interpretation tended to be maintained (Kalick, '77) despite the sanguine results of studies that examined the general degree of satisfaction of those patients who were accepted for plastic surgery. For example, in the previously mentioned Edgerton study (Edgerton *et al.*, '61), all participants were given the surgery they requested regardless of whether or not the psychological screening process would have proscribed it. Although the initial psychological assessment procedure diagnosed only about 30% of the sample as normal, well-adapted people, a six-month follow-up study revealed that 94% reported favorable psychological changes following surgery.

Even such impressive results have sometimes been interpreted to mean that good, long-term results of alteration procedures can be obtained only despite the fact that the people seeking the operation are doing so on the basis of neurotic or unrealistic motivations (e.g., Gifford, '72; Kalick, '78). As Kalick observes:

> This is at minimum something of a paradox. The composite picture (of the clinical area) is one of a traveler who misreads his road map and takes a wrong turn, which ultimately transpires to be a shortcut. That this could happen occasionally is not surprising, but that it happens consistently is remarkable. Perhaps patients' motives for surgery are not so unrealistic after all (Kalick, '78).

Only recently, Kalick notes, has the possibility been considered that cosmetic facial alterations improve a patient's appearance and thereby directly enhance his or her social value, and improvement in social value enables them to gain greater social rewards which then results in their leading more satisfying and comfortable lives.

4

The "Social Science" Research Tradition

This possibility has been considered only recently because only recently have social scientists seriously begun to investigate the social and psychological effects of physical appearance. Ten years ago no social scientist could have provided an "overview of psychological effects of physical attractiveness." Today, in 1980, there exists a substantial and still-growing literature addressed to the identification of the psychological effects of differential levels of attractiveness.

A brief overview of the physical attractiveness literature follows. A person's physical attractiveness level has been revealed by numerous investigations to be an extraordinarily important psychological variable, for it has accounted for a statistically significant portion of the variance in almost all situations in which it has been investigated and for almost all dependent measures which have been constructed to show its effect. This effect, in general, is such that the physically attractive are preferred to the unattractive and thus receive numerous preferential social treatments (Berscheid and Walster, '74; Adams and Crossman, '78).

This bird's eye view of the social scientific physical attractiveness literature does not allow scrutiny of the twists, turns, bumps and inconsistencies that are apparent at closer range. (A more detailed examination of some of these is provided by Adams in this volume.) For the purposes of the present paper, however, it is sufficient to state that the psychological effects of physical attractiveness have been found to be pervasive in frequency, considerable in strength, and generally monolithic in nature. Social scientific investigations of the subject have, in fact, added new dimensions to Freud's statement that, "anatomy is destiny."

Reaction to the Social Impact of Physical Attractiveness

There is something that lurks under this formal "bottom line" of the study of the psychological effects of physical attractiveness, however—something that almost no one (at least in social science) talks about, something that almost no one has really investigated, something that may be responsible for the fact that only ten or fifteen years ago an overview of the physical attractiveness literature wasn't possible because none existed, and something that may be partially responsible for the nature of the clinical research tradition. It is also something which may continue to influence both research and related practice in this area. That "something" casting its shadow over the research literature in both the clinical and social scientific areas is the psychological effects of knowledge about, or suspicion of, the *actual* effects of physical attractiveness.

The knowledge or suspicion that our physical attractiveness significantly affects both the quality and course of our lives through how we are treated by others appears to cause us discomfort, distress, uneasiness, and embarrassment. The fact that physical appearance, and particularly whether others find it pleasing or displeasing, should make an important difference in a person's life—from such intimate matters as the quality of their sex life, and who (or if) they marry, to such formal but far-reaching matters as their educational and career opportunities—is not something that makes most of us very comfortable. The fact that social scientists were uncomfortable with the physical attractiveness variable several decades ago is at least partially responsible for their reluctance to investigate it.

There are those who would not agree that it was the sheer discomfort aroused by the suspicion that the physical attractiveness variable *would* account for a good deal of variance along any number of psychological dimensions that led social psychologists to avoid it. Kalick ('78), for example, in his brief history of the social scientific tradition of attractiveness research, states that the reason social scientists were so slow in outlining the psychological impact of physical appearance is not that they were avoiding the subject; rather, he contends, they were simply looking at the wrong physical appearance variables. He points out that the social psychologist Paul Secord and his associates were examining, in the 1950's, the effects of certain physical characteristics (such as mouth curvature, eye depth, etc.) upon impressions of a stimulus person's personality, intelligence, and other characteristics, but that the findings were of little interest outside a small circle of person-perception researchers. Significantly, Kalick doesn't say *why* Secord's findings were of little interest—just that they were. He then attributes the conduct of research directly on physical attractiveness to a revolutionary discovery—to wit:

> [The] . . . uninspiring status quo changed abruptly about ten years ago, with the advent of a development that transformed the ancient if vague concept of physical attractiveness to a powerful research construct. The development was the realization that within our culture judges agree closely on how attractive a given stimulus person is. Indeed, they are able to distinguish many points on the spectrum of attractiveness. So, even though researchers are far from possessing a working definition of beauty, they have been able to use it as a hard-working construct in their research. Investigators can rate their target persons by using judges as human attractiveness meters (Kalick, 1978).

(It might be noted that it would be more precise to use the phrase *facial physical attractiveness*, for very rarely are anything but head-and-shoulder photos used in physical attractiveness studies, although when the stimulus person is evaluated *in vivo*, the results appear to be approximately the same.)

Kalick does not speculate on *why* it took people so long to see that, in our culture, people do agree—far more than they disagree—on a person's physical attractiveness level. One can make a good guess, however, about the source of this blindness. Recognition that people do agree on this matter leads very quickly to important and discomfiting implications. One of these is that the validity of the happy notion that someone, some-where, is going to find any given individual "beautiful" or "handsome" is immediately challenged. Another is that if most everyone agrees on how attractive another is, and if their treatment of that individual is influenced by their perception of his or her physical attractiveness, then that individual's physical appearance is going to make an important difference in their life. Once such agreement is recognized, it is difficult to continue to maintain that "beauty is only skin deep" and, therefore, a superficial characteristic that psychologists need not take into consideration in the prediction of social behavior.

In fairness, it should be noted that there was some suspicion voiced in the 1960's that physical appearance might have more of an influence upon human behavior than was ordinarily recognized. Lindzey ('65), for ex-ample, pointed out psychologists' reluctance to investigate physical ap-pearance variables and attributed it to the fact that American psychology was permeated with an environmentalist philosophy which maintained that most important personal characteristics are molded by the environ-ment—not inherited. Since physical characteristics were believed to be largely inherited and not subject to modification, it was important that these characteristics *not* be significant to life, liberty, and especially to a person's success in the pursuit of happiness; any evidence that they *were* significant could be counted on to cause discomfort. Lindzey also pointed out that many early psychological theories attempted to predict behavior from various bodily characteristics, and they proved to be dismal flops. (The science of phrenology, which sought to predict such psychological characteristics as intelligence and warmth from the bumps on a person's head, being one spectacular example). As a consequence, any attempt to associate behavior with physical characteristics of any kind smacked of charlatanism, and psychologists generally tended to shy away from any such research enterprise.

About five years later, Aronson ('69), a major researcher in the area of interpersonal attraction, also was moved to comment upon neglect of the physical attractiveness variable. He, too, blamed the democratic and en-vironmentalist philosophies so dear to Americans:

> It is difficult to be certain why the effects of physical beauty have not been studied more systematically. It may be that, at some level, we would hate to find evidence that beautiful women are better liked than homely women—somehow this seems undemocratic. In a democracy we like to feel that with

hard work and a good deal of motivation, a person can accomplish almost anything. But, alas (most of us believe), hard work cannot make an ugly woman beautiful. Because of this suspicion perhaps most social psychologists implicitly prefer to believe that beauty is indeed only skin deep—and avoid the investigation of its social impact for fear they might learn otherwise.

With the wisdom conferred by the hindsight of ten years, the way in which Aronson phrased his point is interesting because it unwittingly illustrates how we typically reduce the discomfort aroused by suspicion of the effect of physical attractiveness. Note first that Aronson's comment focuses upon the extreme states of being "beautiful" or "ugly"—not points in-between. Obviously, few people are beautiful or downright ugly, so this is one way of limiting (at least psychologically) the impact of the physical attractiveness variable; if only extreme physical attractiveness or unattractiveness are thought to have an impact, and if physical attractiveness is not thought of as a continuum upon which most everyone can be placed, then the number of people affected, and thus the importance and impact of this variable, is automatically reduced. (My guess is that most of us make this assumption, and since most of us rate ourselves as average or "a little above average" in attractiveness, if we were asked to tell how much our appearance has affected or continues to affect our lives, we probably would say "very little." But this is a question in dire need of investigation.)

There is a second way in which we attempt to limit the impact of physical attractiveness, as Aronson's statement suggests. He focussed his comment exclusively upon women, leaving out men and children. It is still popular to think of physical attractiveness as being important primarily to women and that it is most likely to have its impact upon women in adolescence and young adulthood, particularly in their relationships with young men. Physical attractiveness generally is not thought of as a variable whose impact cuts across all ages, from infancy through old age, and across both sexes, influencing the lives of men as well as women, and across all social-economic stations and situations in life.

The impact of physical attractiveness tends to be popularly thought to be limited to women, even though the very first bit of research on the subject revealed that the physical attractiveness of men is also important. Walster and her associates ('66) constructed a college "computer dance" where the student was assured that with the purchase of a ticket, he or she would get a randomly assigned date to the dance. The date assignments, however, were not random; they were designed to test the "matching hypothesis" of social choice, which was first suggested by sociologist Goffman ('52) who observed that, "A proposal of marriage in our society tends to be a way in which a man sums up his social attributes and suggests to a woman that hers are not so much better as to preclude a merger or partnership in these matters." Reasoning, then, that romantic aspirations with members of the opposite sex are limited by one's own social desirability, the investigators predicted that dates of equal social desirability would like each other more than men and women who were paired with someone who was either more or less socially desirable then they themselves were.

What makes a person socially desirable? The experimenters decided, rather arbitrarily for purposes of their study, that a person's social desirability surely included his or her intelligence, his or her social skills, his or her personality, and finally, and really as an afterthought, a person's physical attractiveness. The way in which a student's physical attractiveness was measured in this study was quick and crude. As the student was buying a ticket to the dance, and as the clerk was accepting the student's money and issuing the ticket, the clerk made a rating of the student's approximate level of physical attractiveness.

The study revealed no support whatsoever for the matching hypothesis of social choice. Not only that, but whether the person was male or female, their intelligence, social skills, and personality had little or nothing to do with how much they were preferred by their partner. Rather, physical attractiveness alone determined how each person reacted to his or her date. Specifically, the more physically attractive the man or woman was, the more he or she was liked by the partner.

If I recall correctly, the original title of the article reporting these results was: "The importance of physical attractiveness in dating behavior: A serendipitous finding." It *was* serendipitous. It was also embarrassing. Fortunately, although the results were of little "theoretical interest" (some thought), they were published. Among other things, what these results did was to give the lie to what people had *said* was important to them in dating and mating (Berscheid and Walster, '74). Although physical attractiveness had been mentioned, it by no means was of the paramount importance it has subsequently been shown to be.

Still, the discomfort such results arouse can be reduced if, from the findings in some studies that a woman's physical attractiveness accounts for more of the variance upon dependent measures than does a man's, a flying leap is taken to the assumption that physical attractiveness isn't important for men. It is.

To take another example of just *how* important physical attractiveness is to both sexes, consider the results of another study, conducted not long after the computer dance study, by Dion and associates ('72). Dion asked young men and women to look at head and shoulder photographs of young men and women (whose physical attractiveness differed) and tell what they believed the personalities of these stimulus persons were like, what kinds of lives they would lead, and so on. In summary, what Dion found was a very robust physical attractiveness stereotype (later corroborated by many other investigators). Physically attractive people, as contrasted to the physically unattractive, were believed to be more sensitive, kind, interesting, strong, poised, modest, sociable, outgoing, exciting, and sexually warm and responsive persons. In addition, it was believed that attractive people will capture better jobs, have more successful marriages, and experience happier and more fulfilling lives than less attractive people. This was true whether the person doing the rating was a man or woman and whether the person being rated was male or female.

The finding of Dion and colleagues was important because it suggested strongly that the impact of a person's physical attractiveness was not limited to adolescence or young adulthood, and it was not limited to interactions with the opposite sex in dating and other romantic situations. Rather, these results suggested that the influence of physical attractiveness was probably pervasive. It also reinforced the fact that physical attractiveness influences the lives of men as well as of women.

Nevertheless, one still sees the topic of physical attractiveness discussed as though it were important primarily for women, leaving men relatively unscathed. It should be noted that it is true that when people are asked to tell how important the physical attractiveness of a member of the opposite sex is in determining their social choices, men are much more likely to say it is important to them in their choice of a woman than women are likely to say it importantly influences their choice of a man. What people *say*, however, should not be confused with what they *do*, especially when they are uncomfortable with the idea that the appearance factor should make any difference at all. As Allen ('76) has observed, those studies which have actually investigated the impact of physical attractiveness upon men's actual social choices and women's actual choices demonstrate very little difference in its influence, and some studies have even found that the physical attractiveness of the male affects a woman's dating choice even more strongly than a woman's physical attractiveness affects a man's dating choice. (These results suggest that women may be even more uncomfortable than men with the notion that appearance makes a difference, but, again, this is an hypothesis in need of investigation.)

Many researchers, then, like laypersons, have wished to find important limitations to the impact of physical attractiveness. We were no exception. Our principal limiting hypothesis (Berscheid and Walster, '74) was that physical attractiveness probably has its effect only briefly upon initial acquaintance, and as people get to know each other, it ceases to be of importance. It was recognized, of course, that even if physical attractiveness was an important variable only in the initial stages of social interaction, it would still be of considerable importance, because many interactions would never be maintained long enough for other attributes of the person to become known, especially when the interaction was terminated due to assumptions about the other person's undesirability made on the basis of their unattractiveness.

The possibility that familiarity with another would erase the impact of their appearance was fastened upon by others, as well. For example, Levinger ('74), a well-known researcher in the attraction and marriage area commented:

> Berscheid and Walster ('72) have reviewed various additional studies showing that good looks elicit favorable attitudes and behavior in a wide variety of interpersonal settings. It remains unclear, however, under what conditions initial impressions of a "beautiful person" are outweighed by subsequent interaction with him or her; or how an "ugly" person may gradually or suddenly become attractive for reasons other than a change in physical appearance. Consider this striking autobiographical excerpt from Nikos Kazantzakis: "When I was five years old, I was taken to some woman, vaguely a teacher, to learn how to draws i's and koulouria on a slate . . . She was a simple peasant type, short and fattish, a little humpbacked, with a wart on the right side of her chin . . . At first, I wanted nothing to do with her. I liked neither her breath nor her hump. But then, though I don't know how, she began to be transformed little by little before my eyes: The wart disappeared, her back straightened, her flabby body grew slim and beautiful, and finally after a few weeks, she became a slender angel wearing a snow-white tunic and holding an immense bronze trumpet . . . Angel and Madame Teacher had become one."

This happy hypothesis was finally submitted to test by Mathes ('75), who asked college-aged men and women to sign a contract to complete five dates during the course of an experiment. He then randomly assigned men and women to each other with the restriction that all possible combinations of physical attractiveness levels (as well as levels of a personality factor he was interested in) were created. Mathes hypothesized that on the first date, and possibly the second, attractiveness would—as it had been demonstrated in so many previous studies—strongly determine the liking for the date; but on later dates, after the young men and women had become thoroughly acquainted with each other, physical attractiveness would dissipate as a factor in attraction. However, Mathes' data did not confirm the hypothesis. In fact, instead of attractiveness becoming *less* important as a determinant of liking across five dates, attractiveness increased in importance from the first date to subsequent dates.

Other investigators have directed their research toward discovering yet other limits of the impact of physical attractiveness. Allen ('78), for example, reasoned that physical attractiveness seemed to be more powerful

11

than other factors in its influence upon social choice merely because its impact had not been compared with other very powerful factors. He proceeded to make such experimental comparisons. For the most part, however, Allen's research program has simply added further documentation to previous findings demonstrating that physical attractiveness is, indeed, a very potent factor, especially in heterosexual social choice. For example, Allen and Meredith (as described in Allen, '78) compared the importance of "independence" and "honesty" to physical attractiveness as criteria for dating choices. They found that although a person's degree of honesty affected dating choice, physical attractiveness was far more important. Independence was not significant at all, nor did trustworthiness manage to hold its own against attractiveness (Shepherd and Allen, as described in Allen, '78); physically attractive women received very high ratings as desirable dates whether they were trustworthy or not. Finally, and interestingly, Allen ('76) pitted a person's physical attractiveness against similarity of racial background as a factor in dating choice. This time, physical attractiveness met its match—especially for women; that is, while women showed highly significant effects for *both* race and attractiveness in their dating choices, white women preferred to date white men and gave race more weight than attractiveness in making their choices. This was not true, however, for white males; while they also preferred to date attractive persons of their own race, a woman's physical attractiveness was more important to them than was her race.

Some limitations and qualifications to the rule that the physically attractive are socially preferred to the unattractive and are treated better have been found (and are outlined by Adams in this volume), but they *are* exceptions to the general rule. And, as one might expect, this differential treatment leaves its mark on the individual's personality, social skills, educational and career opportunities, social and intimate life, and perhaps even on their spiritual life.

That one's appearance may affect one's mental and spiritual health was, interestingly enough, the subject of Mary Shelley's tale, written in 1917, about the young medical student who created a monster. The social commentator and syndicated columnist Sidney Harris recently reminded his readers that it was not the monster who was named Frankenstein (as many tend to suppose), but rather the medical student who created him. Further, the tale was not conceived to be a horror story in the supernatural sense, but rather a horror story in the moral sense. For the monster was not originally evil when it came to life. To the contrary, like all of us, it yearned for human sympathy, affection, and understanding. The monster, in fact, expressed hope (as Shelley put the words in the monster's mouth) " . . . to meet with beings who, pardoning my outward form, would love me for the excellent qualities I was capable of unfolding . . . " But, of course, the creature the young scientist created was shunned by everyone who came into contact with it, because his outward form was alien, revolting, and repulsive. As a result of this treatment, the creature ultimately killed the scientist's brother, the brother's wife, as well as the scientist himself—truly becoming a monster whose inner character was congruent with his outward appearance. He sadly says at the end, "I cannot believe that I am the same creature whose thoughts were once filled with sublime and transcended visions of the beauty and majesty of goodness. But it is even so . . . the fallen angel becomes a malignant devil."

Fairy tales and horror stories frequently exaggerate to make their moral points. The actual process by which differential treatment of people according to their outward appearance may mold their character and behavior is more subtle than in the story of Frankenstein but undoubtedly just as effective. Consider, for example, a study that was performed by Snyder and co-workers ('77). The procedure was simple: Men and women were asked to become acquainted with one another over the telephone. Some of the men, however (and unbeknownst to the women), were led to believe (via a photograph) that the woman they were to talk to was physically attractive, while others were led to believe that the woman they were to talk to was physically unattractive. The man and woman then talked, and each side of the telephone conversation was recorded on separate channels. Outside observers (who knew nothing of the study or the circumstances of the conversation) were then asked to to listen to each woman's contribution to the conversation and to tell what kind of a person she was. The results revealed, in self-fulfilling prophecy fashion, that a woman who was talking to a man who believed that she was physically attractive was judged, on the basis of her verbal behavior alone, to be more poised, more sociable, more vivacious, and so on, than was a woman who was talking to a man who believed her to be physically unattractive. It is clear, then, that by their own differential behavior, the men brought out of the women the very behavior that they expected the women to demonstrate.

It should be added that people were also asked to listen to the men's contributions to the conversation. Interestingly, the men who thought they were interacting with a physically attractive woman were judged by outside observers, simply on the basis of their contribution to the conversation, to be more sociable, more sexually warm, more interesting, more independent, more sexually permissive, more bold, more outgoing and humorous, and more socially adept than were men who believed themselves to be talking to a physically unattractive woman. Another person's degree of physical attractiveness clearly affects our own behavior; and that behavior in turn affects the other person's behavior, in a rather vicious cycle.

13

The method used in this study is one way to investigate the impact of a person's physical attractiveness level on his or her behavior. The more usual and less satisfactory route is to take a few handfuls of people, measure their physical attractiveness levels, and run a correlation between those attractiveness measurements and measurements of their personality or behavioral characteristics. Such studies have found a number of differences between the attractive and unattractive. For example, and as one would expect, a number of investigators (Berscheid *et al.*, '71; Allen and Wroble, '75; Mathes and Kahn, '75) have found a significant relationship between a person's physical attractiveness level and their self-esteem. Self-esteem is an important psychological variable which is associated with a variety of behaviors, both social and moral (e.g., Aronson and Mettee, '68). Also, and not unexpectedly, attractive people seem to be more socially active than unattractive people are (Berscheid *et al.*, '71; Krebs and Adinolfi, '75; Tinken, as described in Allen, '78), and they seem to have more social skills and be more assertive than the unattractive (Jackson and Huston, '75; Goldman and Lewis, '77).

The problem with this sort of study, however, is that one can never be entirely confident that physical attractiveness is solely—or even primarily—responsible for the differences observed. This tends to be true of almost all correlational studies, where third variables may be responsible for the observed relationship. It is especially true, however, when physical attractiveness is one of the major variables, because attractiveness is known to be associated (slightly, but significantly) with intelligence and health factors—factors which should have generally the same directional impact physical attractiveness does. (See Berscheid and Walster, '74, for a discussion of this point.)

The impact of a person's physical attractiveness level, then, is probably more unequivocally assessed either in the experimental laboratory or in the laboratory of nature where relatively quick and dramatic alterations of one's physical attractiveness level, both for the better and for the worse, take place—sometimes by accident and other times by design. Quite obviously, the impact of physical attractiveness might well be assessed using a "before-after" design in those situations.

The relative scarcity of such systematic studies, however (excluding anecdotal case reports which use a variety of dependent measures designed primarily to assess psychopathology), brings me back to my theme—which is simply that the fact that a person's physical attractiveness makes an important difference in how society treats them and is thus a major factor in the quality of their lives along myriad dimensions, is not a fact with which we are comfortable. It is, as a consequence, a fact whose truth we tend to minimize and deny. This denial, in turn, affects the kinds of investigations we conduct and the kinds of conclusion we reach.

I have discussed some of the ways in which I believe our discomfort with the impact of physical attractiveness has influenced research in the social scientific tradition, but I suspect it has no less influenced research within the clinical tradition. It is very easy, for example, to arrive at the hypothesis that anyone who requests surgery or other procedures to improve their appearance is probably a neurotic or borderline personality *if* one believes that physical attractiveness does not make much of a difference in a person's life. Under such circumstances, it is easy to maintain that it is only a misguided (or neurotic) belief that appearance makes a difference, or perhaps some sort of quixotic vanity that drives people to the surgeon—facial, oral or otherwise—or to the orthodontist, or to any of the persons in the business of making facial and body alterations. Research within the clinical tradition might have taken quite a different tack were society not so enamored of the idea that because a person's appearance *ought* not to make a difference, it *does* not—except in unusual cases. Specifically, there might be many more systematic investigations of how facial alterations affect the perception that others have of the individual, the way in which the individual is treated by others before the alteration and after, and, thus, what kind of differences in behavior the individual might be expected to demonstrate in reaction to these differences in treatment from others. On the basis of such information, individuals might be better prepared to cope with the social consequences of the alteration.

A study conducted by Kalick ('77) is an example of such a study. Kalick's study was patterned very closely after the study done by Dion and colleagues ('72) described earlier, in that young men and women examined photographs and rated the persons depicted along a number of dimensions. The difference in Kalick's study, however, was that he used photographs of eight individuals before they had actually experienced cosmetic surgery and photos of them after the surgery had been performed.

The source of these photographs were journals of plastic surgery and professional textbooks on the subject, for it was assumed that these would represent the state of the art of cosmetic surgery and demonstrate the most up-to- date innovations in technique on the part of highly competent surgeons. In choosing the actual photographs to be used, Kalick stipulated that the stimulus persons must be of college age and within the normal range of appearance, even in the pre- surgery photograph. In addition, all of the photographs had to be only a profile view of the entire face, each had to be presentable as a snapshot with no hint that the person photographed had had plastic surgery, and all pre- and post-operative pairs of photographs had to show the same pose and present as little change of detail as possible. As a result of all these restrictions, Kalick found suitable

15

only a number of photographs of females, so the results of the study, regrettably, apply directly only to females.

Those who participated in the study were asked to look at the photographs and to rate the person depicted along a number of dimensions, as in the Dion study. In addition, they were asked to tell: "How likely is it that she will marry the man of her choice?"; "If she does marry, how likely is it that she will be an understanding partner in marriage?"; "How likely is it that she will be a warm, responsive sexual partner in marriage?"; and to answer questions concerning the person's likely social and professional happiness. Participants also were asked to tell to what extent they thought they would personally like or dislike the person and the extent to which they would enjoy working together with the person on a mutual task—or, in other words, how personally attracted they were to the individual depicted. Finally, since each participant evaluated three people, they were asked which of the three stimulus persons would be his or her first choice for an actual meeting and which would be the second choice.

The results of this study are interesting for a number of reasons. First, there is the question of whether cosmetic surgery actually increased the physical attractiveness level of the individuals who were depicted in the photos. Kalick found that, indeed, it had. According to pre-tests in which the physical attractiveness of the stimulus persons were evaluated, all were found to show a statistically significant improvement in appearance following surgery. Although statistically significant, this improvement was of moderate magnitude. On the other hand, it is interesting that virtually all of the persons depicted moved from the negative side of a neutral point on a physical attractiveness scale (where they were before surgery) to the positive side of the physical attractiveness scale (after surgery), except in one case (where a person moved very close to neutrality from a highly unattractive point).

Second, there is the question of whether this change in appearance resulted in the stimulus person's being perceived differently in terms of her personality and other characteristics. It did. The perceived social desirability of the personality of the stimulus person significantly increased after surgery. After surgery, the women were perceived to be kinder, more sensitive, more sexually warm and responsive, and so on, than they were before surgery. In addition, they were perceived to be more competent marriage partners and more likely to marry the person of their choice after surgery than before surgery. Further, there was a significant change in their perceived social and professional happiness after surgery. Finally, each rater's estimate of how much they would personally *like* the individual, how much they would *like working* with them on some task, and how much they would actually *like to meet* with them changed significantly, in a positive direction. This study suggests, then, that cosmetic surgery patients, even those whose state before surgery is not anywhere near the unattractive end of the continuum, ought to start receiving concrete social benefits from their improved physical appearance immediately following surgery.

Reactions to Improvements in Appearance

How are these benefits going to be received? What is the reaction of the person who experiences the alteration going to be, particularly if the alteration was instigated for reasons of physical health rather than for sheer aesthetic reasons? It is not unusual to suggest that facial alteration brings psychological distress when the change has been in a negative direction. It is easy to understand how bewildering it must be for a person, who is the same person they have always been—in intelligence, in attitudes, in behavior, in likes and dislikes—to suddenly be treated very differently simply because their outward form has changed unfavorably. This is a Frankensteinian nightmare, indeed.

But I should like to suggest that while everyone likes to be treated well, improvement in one's treatment by others as a result of improvement in appearance is not necessarily going to be an unalloyed delight for some cosmetic surgery patients; in fact, it might sometimes be a source of pain and bewilderment. The source of the bewilderment and discomfort— perhaps even of surprise at the extent of the differential treatment—is, again, our collective discomfort with the notion that physical attractiveness *does* have more of an influence on our lives than we would like to believe. It must be discomfiting to discover how much we may be liked for our appearance rather than for what we consider to be our more enduring qualities. This is illustrated in an anecdote told by Theodore Reik ('56), the noted psychoanalyst:

> A man once asked his mistress whether she would love him if he were suddenly to become poor. "Of course," she answered. Then he asked whether she would love him if he became crippled by an accident. This question, too, was answered in the affirmative. But still the man was not satisfied. He tried again, asking whether her affection would be the same if, in addition to these handicaps, he were to become deaf, blind, and insane. The woman finally became impatient and said, "Why in the world should I love an impoverished, crippled, deaf and blind idiot?"

One can sympathize with the man. Each of us wants to be loved for ourselves, for the quintessence of us. We cannot always say exactly what that quintessence is, but we frequently know what it is *not*. Our ideas of who we really are often do not include the material resources we happen to enjoy at the moment, our social status and prestige, and especially does not often include what we look like. Most of us—at least those who have *not* experienced swift alterations of physical appearance—can continue to believe that our physical attractiveness level plays a minor role in how we are treated by others. It is harder, however, for those who have actually experienced swift changes in appearance to continue to deny and to minimize the influence of physical attractiveness in their own lives—and this fact may be disturbing, even when the changes are for the better.

Some might want to argue that while positive changes in appearance may affect treatment of the person by strangers or new acquaintances, they are much less likely to have an impact upon such long-standing relationships as marital relationships. However, this is unlikely given that the number of social alternatives available to a person are known to increase with increases in physical attractiveness and that the number of alternatives to the present relationship is an extraordinarily important factor in the prediction of its longevity and stability, as well as satisfaction with it (Berscheid and Campbell, in press). In fact, it is changes in long-standing relationships that might be especially distressing to both the individual who has experienced a facial alteration and to those with whom the individual closely interacts.

IMPLICATIONS FOR FUTURE RESEARCH

It has been argued that discomfort with the fact that physical appearance has an important impact on our lives has affected both the social scientific and clinical research traditions on this matter and that it probably continues to affect our thinking on the subject. It also seems reasonable to predict that it will affect the kind of research that will be done on the topic in the future, both by social scientists and clinicians, as well as the myriad front-line judgments clinical practitioners must make. This is unfortunate, because good information is needed more now than ever before. The number of cosmetic surgical operations in the United States rose from 15,000 in 1949 to nearly one million in 1971 (Macgregor, '74), and surely has risen astronomically within the past nine years. Some of this is, no doubt, accountable for by improved insurance coverage and improved technology for making appearance alterations, facial and otherwise. Apparently, however, even people in the alteration business are themselves uncomfortable with this rise—or, more accurately, uncomfortable with the implications of the rise. For example, Goulian, a prominent plastic surgeon, is quoted as saying that:

> Cosmetic surgery is a service for people who *need* it. The need has been made acute because of our society's enormous preoccupation with youth and

18

beauty. I find this disturbing because any culture we really know enough about has gone through a similar preoccupation before its imminent decline. The Romans went through this; the Greeks went through this. It was manifest just before they fell apart at the seams (*Town and Country*, October 1979).

The reasoning underlying this comment seems to be: a) physical attractiveness *ought not* to make a difference; b) it clearly *does* make a difference, as evidenced not only by social scientific research but by the enormous increase in the practice of procedures that alter physical form and attractiveness level, including an eight billion dollar cosmetic industry; and, c) therefore, we are in a period of moral decay.

Whether or not this is a period of moral decay, it seems hasty to pin the evergrowing importance of physical attractiveness in our society simply upon immorality, or affluence, or increases in technology which permit such alterations to be made. Relatedly, it is doubtful that either the Greeks or the Romans ever went through what people are going through today. Rather, I suspect that much of the growth of the importance of physical attractiveness is due to our increased geographic mobility, as well as the concentration of our population in large urban areas. Because of these factors, people are now subject to many more one-time or few-time interactions with other people than ever before. This is true for children as well as for adults. For example, only 57.4% of families in the United States lived at the same address in 1970 and 1974 (which indicates that people must frequently change friends, children have to change schools and playmates, and so on), and it is estimated that the average young person of age 20 years entering the job market today will change jobs at least seven times during his working years (Lynch, '77). In addition, the divorce rate in this country has increased some 700% since the turn of the century, and estimations of the probable longevity of current marriages has decreased radically (Berscheid and Campbell, in press). Further, the divorce rates for marriages with and without children have been converging, and the re-marriage rates make it more likely than ever before that children will have at least one set, if not more, of step-parents and associated relatives and step-siblings.

In a society in which one cannot even count on having the same set of parents for any length of time, the same marriage partner for any length of time, when one may be thrown in to the dating and mating market at age 30, 40, 50, or even 60, when it becomes increasingly unlikely that one will have the same workmates, colleagues or neighbors for any length of time—in sum, in a society in which social fragmentation has proceeded to an unprecedented point (Slater, '70), people are constantly assessed very quickly by others simply on the basis of their appearance rather than upon their record of actual behavior and other characteristics. Is it any wonder, then, that to help them cope, people look to the new keepers of the fountain of beauty and youth—the dentists, the doctors, the plastic surgeons, the nutritionists, the cosmeticians, the physical therapists, and so on?

The fragmentation of society and its implications for the increased importance of physical attractiveness should affect all of us equally. There is another factor, however, that may have acted to increase the importance of physical attractiveness differentially for men. With increasing economic and legal independence of women has come unprecedented social independence—the freedom to choose to interact socially, to date and to marry men for reasons other than the need for a meal ticket, for social position and for security. Women, then, increasingly choose to date and mate for many of the same reasons men have been using for years to make their social choices among the opposite sex, and most importantly among these reasons has been romantic love.

To illustrate, Kephart ('67) asked men and women of prime marital age "If a man (or woman) had all the other qualities you desired, would you marry this person if you were not in love with him (her)?" A decade or so ago, Kephart found that 65% of the men in his sample said no. Romantic love for the majority of men, then, was a necessary condition for marriage. However, only 24.3% of the Kephart's women respondents said no. Kephart and others concluded from these data that while men could afford the luxury of contracting a marriage on the basis of the existence of a strong sentiment, women used other, more pragmatic, considerations as criteria for entering the marriage contract.

A decade later, Campbell and Berscheid ('76) replicated Kephart's study on a subject population comparable to his on all reported characteristics. Of the men in the sample, 86% said no to the critical question. This represents an increase of 21% over the past decade of men who believe romantic love to be a necessary condition for marriage. The most dramatic change, however, was for women respondents. As compared to Kephart's figure of 24%, 80% of the women in our sample said no, representing an increase of 56% of women who now believe being in love is a necessary condition for marriage. If the respondents' reports are congruent with their behavior, it is now the case that not one, but both principals of most marriage contracts are using the existence of a strong emotion, romantic love, as a necessary basis for the marriage.

What does romantic love have to do with physical attractiveness? A great deal. When romantic love becomes an important factor in social choice, physical attractiveness appears to become important also. This is especially true in our own culture, as Ellis documented ('54) in his survey of the content of the media:

20

The only thing most consistently emphasized and embellished in today's most popular publications and productions is not, as you might think, sex, nor love, nor marriage. It is, rather, the great American prerequisite to sex, love, and marriage—feminine pulchritude.

"Feminine pulchritude," Ellis said in 1954. For 1984, "male pulchritude" looms as a prerequisite for the remainder of the population. For as Paul Rosenblatt ('74) has observed: " . . . impractical grounds in choice of spouse (largely beauty) correlate .70 (p < .01) with freedom of choice of spouse, which suggests that beauty is important only where people must choose spouses on their own and perhaps where decisions are difficult and not easily justified on more practical grounds." This suggests that greater emphasis on female physical attractiveness cross-culturally and over time may have been a rather direct result of the lesser power of the female and lack of freedom of choice in mate selection. In any event, one can argue that the recent phenomena of male nude centerfolds and male nude dancers are evidence that women are now free to choose dates and mates on grounds as frivolous as has been typical of the male. As a consequence, we can also predict that the pressure for better, cheaper, faster, and less painful procedures by which to make facial alterations is not likely to decrease, nor is the use of what procedures are currently available.

The social psychologist may more confidently discuss why and how physical attractiveness makes a difference than the source of our discomfort that it does. In this regard, I should like to suggest that only two things are certain:

First, in any heaven I have ever heard of, in any religion or set of spiritual beliefs, we are all disembodied spirits—we may retain our same personality, our "souls", or the sum total of all the behaviors we have ever exhibited, but flesh and bone have melted away and we are judged, just as dogs and cats and very small children in this world judge us, simply on the basis of our behavior.

Second, this is not heaven. It therefore probably helps neither us nor others to pretend that it is by denying the role that physical form plays in people's lives.

REFERENCES

Adams, G. R. and S. M. Crossman. *Physical Attractiveness: A Cultural Imperative.* Libra Publishing, Roslyn Heights, New York, 1978.

Allen, B. P. Race and physical attractiveness as criteria for white subjects' dating choices. Soc. Behav. Personal. *4*:289-296, 1976.

Allen, B. P. *Social Behavior: Fact and Falsehood.* Nelson Hall, Chicago, 1978.

21

Psychological Effects of Physical Attractiveness

Allen, B. P. and S. Wroble. Attractive people like themselves better than unattractive people—most of the time: Self-descriptions employing the AGT. Paper presented at the Midwestern Psychological Association Convention, 1975.

Aronson, E. Some antecedents of interpersonal attraction. In: *Nebraska Symposium on Motivation*, W. J. Arnold and D. Levine (eds.). University of Nebraska Press, Lincoln, Nebraska, 1969.

Aronson, E. and D. R. Mettee. Dishonest behavior as a function of differential levels of induced self- esteem. J. Personal. Soc. Psych. *9*:121-127, 1968.

Baker, W. and L. Smith. Facial disfigurement and personality. J. A. M. A. *112*:301-304, 1939.

Berscheid, E. and B. Campbell. Longevity of close relationships in a period of rapid social change. In: *The Justice Motive in Times of Scarcity and Change*. M. Lerner (ed.), Plenum, New York, in press.

Berscheid, E., K. Dion, E. Walster and G. W. Walster. Physical attractiveness and dating choice: A test of the matching hypothesis. J. Exp. Soc. Psych. *7*:173-180, 1971.

Berscheid, E. and E. Walster. Physical attractiveness. In: *Advances in Experimental Social Psychology* (Vol. 7), L. Berkowitz (ed.). Academic Press, New York, 1974.

Dion, K., E. Berscheid and E. Walster. What is beautiful is good. J. Personal. Soc. Psych. *24*:285-290, 1972.

Edgerton, M., W. Jacobson and E. Meyer. Surgical- psychiatric study of patients seeking plastic (cosmetic) surgery: Ninety-eight consecutive patients with minimal deformity. Brit. J. Plast. Surg. *13*:136-145, 1961

Ellis, A. *The American Sexual Tragedy*. Twayne Publishers, New York, 1954.

Gifford, S. Cosmetic surgery and personality change: A review and some clinical observations. In: *The Unfavorable Result in Plastic Surgery: Avoidance and Treatment*. , R. Goldwyn (ed.), Little, Brown and Co., Boston, 1972.

Goffman, E. On cooling the mark out: Some aspects of adaptation to failure. Psychiatry *15*:451-463, 1952.

Goldman, W. and P. Lewis. Beautiful is good: Evidence that the physically attractive are more socially skillful. J. Exp. Soc. Psych. *13*:125-130, 1977.

Hill, G. and G. Silver. Psychodynamic and esthetic motivations for plastic surgery. Psychosomatic Med. *12*:345-355, 1950.

Jackson, D. and T. L. Huston. Physical attractiveness and assertiveness. J. Soc. Psych. *95*:79-84, 1975.

Kalick, S. M. Plastic surgery, physical appearance, and person perception. Unpublished doctoral dissertation, Harvard University, 1977.

Kalick, S. M. Toward an interdisciplinary psychology of appearances. Psychiatry *41*(3):243-253, 1978.

Kephart, W. M. Some correlates of romantic love. J. Marr. Fam., 470-474, 1967.

Krebs, D. and A. A. Adinolfi. Physical attractiveness, social relations, and personality style. J. Personal. Soc. Psych. *31*:245-253, 1975.

Levinger, G. A three-level approach to attraction: Toward an understanding of pair relatedness. In: *Foundations of Interpersonal Attraction*, T. L. Huston (ed.). Academic Press, New York, 1974.

Lindzey, G. Morphology and behavior. In: *Theories of Personality: Primary Sources and Research*, G. Lindzey and C. S. Hall (eds.). Wiley and Sons, New York, 1965.

Lynch. J. J. *The Broken Heart: The Medical Consequences of Loneliness*. Basic Books, New York, 1977.

Macgregor, F. *Transformation and Identity*. New York Times Book Co., New York, 1974.

Mathes, E. W. The effects of physical attractiveness and anxiety on heterosexual attraction over a series of five encounters. J. Marr. Fam., 769-773, 1975.

Mathes, E. W. and A. Kahn. Physical attractiveness, happiness, neuroticism, and self-esteem. J. Psych. *90*:27-30, 1975.

Meredith, M. The influence of physical attractiveness, independence and honesty on date selection. Unpublished paper, Western Illinois University, 1972.

Peck, H. and S. Peck. A concept of facial esthetics. Angle Orthod. *40*(4):284-317, 1970.

Reik, T. *A Psychologist Looks at Love*. Lancer Books, New York, 1944.

Rosenblatt, P. C. Cross-cultural perspective on attraction. In: *Foundations of Interpersonal Attraction*, T. L. Huston (ed.), Academic Press, New York, 1974.

Shepard, M. The effects of physical attractiveness and trustworthiness in long- and short-term dating selection. Unpublished paper. Western Illinois University, 1973.

Slater, P. *The Pursuit of Loneliness.*, Beacon Press, Boston, 1970.

Snyder, M., E. D. Tanke and E. Berscheid. Social perception and interpersonal behavior: On the self-fulfilling nature of social stereotypes. J. Personal. Soc. Psych. *35*:656-666, 1977.

Tinken, P. L. Testing for a reality basis to the "beautiful-is-good" stereotype. Master's thesis, Western Illinois University, 1976.

Walster, E., V. Aronson, D. Abrahams and L. Rottman. Importance of physical attractiveness in dating behavior. J. Personal. Soc. Psych. *4*:508-516, 1966.

THE EFFECTS OF PHYSICAL ATTRACTIVENESS ON THE SOCIALIZATION PROCESS

Gerald R. Adams, M.A., Ph.D.

Associate Professor and Chairman
Department of Family and Human Development
Utah State University

One of the primary goals of social science is the study of socialization. While numerous theories exist to explain this social process, the general assumption is that societal forces, through varying influences, help to shape the social nature of each individual. Therefore, the study of socialization, as the word implies, is the study of the effects of social interaction and exchange upon individual development and behavior. Historically, sociologists, psychologists, child developmentalists and others have emphasized a perspective which has assumed a unidirectional influence in the socialization process. That is, it has been thought that children are influenced by others but apparently have little counter-influence upon their influencers. This perspective, however, is slowly changing. Although there is contemporary recognition that children influence adults as much as adults influence children, this perspective has not, until recent years, been a highly acceptable viewpoint.

It might seem obvious that a child's temperamental characteristics or social behavior would have certain predictable influences upon an adult caregiver's interaction style with his or her child. However, the influence of morphology in normally developing children may be less intuitively obvious. In recent years, attention has been turned toward the study of morphological influences and has been referred to as the developmental social psychology of physical appearance (Adams, '77a; Adams and Crossman, '78). Evidence indicates that subjective evaluations of body morphology, commonly called physical attractiveness, can influence an individual's social experience and have potential channeling effects upon social and personality development. Also, evidence exists to suggest that physical attractiveness has an impact upon social experience for both children and adults. Thus, physical appearance can potentially influence the socialization process over the full life cycle.

In the remaining pages of this chapter, I will summarize the existing research literature and demonstrate that physical appearance has a strong and important influence upon (a) social impressions and attributions, (b) social exchange and interaction, (c) personality development and (d) social behavior. In the closing pages, I will address the issue of *when* physical appearance emerges as an important socialization variable.

SOCIAL IMPRESSIONS AND ATTRIBUTIONS

Is it possible that we live in a world where physical appearance plays such an influential role that facial and body attractiveness assert a global social impression that biases our initial contact with others? Are we swayed by our subjective evaluation of facial esthetics in stereotypic and predictable ways? My own entry into research addressing these questions was due to a personal reaction to a study reported by Clifford and Walster ('73). In this investigation, it was reported that teachers' expectations for their pupils' school performances were highly influenced by the attractiveness of the children. Attractive children were found to elicit higher teacher expectations than those who were less attractive. As a former elementary school teacher, I questioned the results of this investigation and initiated a series of studies to challenge the findings of the Clifford and Walster investigation. After several studies with preschool teachers (Adams, '78; Adams and Crane, '80), elementary school educators (Adams and LaVoie, '74, '75, '77; LaVoie and Adams, '74), and kindergarten, fourth and seventh grade instructors (Adams and Cohen, '74), I have concluded that Clifford and Walster were right. Teachers are swayed in their individual expectations of children's classroom performance by a child's physical appearance. Simply put, attractive children live in an educational world where teachers have a high expectation for their academic performance. Related research suggests important consequences for attractive children due to this elevated expectation level. Teachers appear prone to give attractive children more information, better evaluations, more opportunity to perform, and more support for their educational endeavors (Adams and LaVoie, '77).

However, does the assumption that attractive individuals are more capable generalize to cover other social behaviors? In an influential study designed to confirm a physical attractiveness stereotype, Dion and co-workers ('72) confirmed that attractiveness strongly affects social impressions central to a variety of personal and social behaviors. In this study, the investigators confirmed what they have called the *beauty-is-good hypothesis*. Other investigations with young children, (Dion, '73; Dion and Berscheid, '74; Adams and Crane, '80), college students (Miller, '70a, '70b; Dion et al., '72) and adults (Adams and Huston, '75) have confirmed that social impressions are substantially based upon a beauty-is-good hypothesis. Individuals judged as physically attractive are viewed, in contrast to their less attractive peers, as socially outgoing and likeable (Adams and Huston, '75; Langlois and Stephan, '77; Lucker et al., '80) poised, confident, and kind (Dion et al., '72; Adams and Huston, '75; McKelvie and Matthews, '76; Hill and Lando, '76) with projected high educational and occupational status (Dion et al., '72; Adams and LaVoie, '75).

Does physical attractiveness have only positive influences upon social impressions or are there undesirable impressions associated with beauty? According to an investigation by Dermer and Thiel ('75), all that glitters may not be gold. That is, beauty may be associated with several desirable social impressions, but attractive individuals are also likely to be seen as egotistical, snobbish and vain. Hence, physical attractiveness can generate an impression of self-centeredness (Wilson et al., '78) which has been defined as a case in point "when beauty may fail" (Dermer and Thiel, '75). There may also be notable exceptions when "unattractiveness blossoms", resulting in positive social impressions. In some of our earlier research efforts (Adams and Huston, '75) we found that while attractive individuals are perceived as possessing higher self-esteem, more prestigious occupational status and greater social extroversion, unattractive individuals, women in particular, are viewed as more honest and moral. Similar findings may emerge in time which likewise support a positive unattractiveness attribution hypothesis.

Although physical attractiveness is associated with certain well-documented social impressions, until recently it has been unclear when the biasing effect of physical appearance actually emerges as an influential factor in social impressions. Cross and Cross ('71) originally documented that 7-, 12-, and 17-year-olds and adults held similar perceptions in their judgments of persons who were or were not physically attractive. These data suggest that a common cultural standard exists for beauty judgments for children and adults. While an investigation by Dion ('73) suggests that three-year-olds utilize a facial attractiveness stereotype in their social impressions, Cavior and Lombardi ('73) have argued that the stereotype does not emerge until early elementary school age. However, other evidence suggests preschool children's social interactions are influenced by their peers' physical appearance. Dion and Berscheid ('74) have demonstrated that children's peer perceptions are influenced by a child's attractiveness and that physical attractiveness functions as an incentive in capturing preschool children's visual attention (Dion, '77). However, the Adams and Crane study ('80) indicates that while preschool children are capable of identifying an attractive child or adult from an unattractive one, this does not assure they will use the beauty-is-good hypothesis in their social behavior. Young children labeled attractive individuals as nicer than their unattractive counterparts, but the pre-school children sampled in this study failed to use a physical attractiveness stereotype in their social play preference. Collectively, these data suggest that children as young as 3 and 4 years of age are potentially influenced by physical attractiveness, although they may only manifest the stereotype in their social attribution behavior. Further socialization experiences may be necessary before the preschool child internalizes the stereotype into their actual social behavior.

Why are children and adults influenced by physical attractiveness? A content analysis of self-report data provided by college students suggests that there are several factors which account for the positive social attributions associated with physical attractiveness (Adams and Crossman, '78). In fact, seven factors accounted for a full 100% of the responses. Attractiveness was viewed as being associated with social status, self-esteem and social/occupational success. Attractive mates were thought to provide an important influence on hereditary factors associated with bearing offspring. As one respondent openly stated, "The more attractive the other member, the more attractive the children will be—making them more socially acceptable." Other respondents suggested that the mass media gears societal members toward assuming that beauty is associated with status and acceptability. Still others assumed that attractiveness ensures other desirable qualities. As one woman said, "When one person perceives another as looking nice, it is often generalized to being nice." Finally, it was not uncommon for attractiveness to be viewed as satisfying a complementary need. For example, one student remarked:

> Physical attractiveness is a strong determinant of attraction because a person's body language—facial wrinkles, choice of clothes and even body build and posture—are all excellent indicators of personality and compatibility; we tend to pick what would be complementary to us.

While a reward-value factor may account for the motivational mechanisms behind the attractiveness social stereotype, recent efforts to look at implicit personality theory may give us additional insight into the role physical attributes may play in determining the attractiveness stereotype. According to Schneider ('73) each of us functionally relate to others in a manner explained by a "naive, implicit personality theory." This theory assumes that in judging others we are inclined to maintain that certain social characteristics covary with specific attributes, although there is not immediate evidence for such an assumption. For example, if Susan views John as being warm, she might also assume he is intelligent, successful and interpersonally adept, even though she has no immediate information on which to base such an assumption. Facial features, emotional expression or physical attractiveness can serve as central attributes (*e.g.*, warmth, which elicits peripheral trait assumptions, such as intelligence or success). Hence, based upon a social stereotype judgment, physical appearance may elicit the added belief that beauty-is-good.

In sum, physical attractiveness is thought to function as a central attribute which elicits implicit assumptions about other attributes. The possession of body attributes which are judged to be physically attractive elicits positive attributions of goodness and negative attributions of vanity and self-centeredness. In other words, beautiful people stimulate stereotypic expectations of specific behavioral attributes that may not actually exist.

SOCIAL EXCHANGE AND INTERACTION

Although social impressions are influenced by the beauty-is-good hypothesis, and social attributions based on physical attractiveness are readily made, evidence suggests that an individual's physical appearance can affect interpersonal interactions as well. Data may be limited by methodological or measurement and sampling problems, but a growing body of research indicates that facial attractiveness may have both facilitative and inhibitive effects upon social exchange. Further, physical attractiveness stereotype effects may actually emerge shortly after birth and remain functional throughout life.

Early Socialization Experiences

For more than three decades, ethologists have been proposing that physical characteristics function as elicitors of approach behavior among humans (Lorenz, '43; Eibl-Eibesfeldt, '70). Recent investigations into infant-adult interaction patterns suggest that an infant's physical characteristics can have profound effects upon their caregiver's attitudes and behavior. Corter and co-workers ('78) have demonstrated that nurses of premature infants give a higher intellectual prognosis when the infant is perceived as physically attractive. Further, college students and teachers are likely to maintain longer visual attention toward attractive versus unattractive infants (Hildebrandt and Fitzgerald, '77). Likewise, some evidence suggests that an infant's physical attractiveness is predictive of the quality of the relationship with a parent (Hildebrandt, '76; Boukydis, '77). Collectively, these studies suggest that as early as infancy, physical attractiveness may have profound influences upon parental attitudes, expectations and interpersonal behavior with their infants.

Other evidence also supports the suggestion that parental behavior may be influenced by a child's perceived physical attractiveness. A colleague and I (Adams and LaVoie, '75) found that parents hold expectations that attractive children will obtain more personal and social success. Further, at least with male elementary school age children, it was noted that mothers and fathers tend to anticipate more use of inductive reasoning as the primary disciplinary style in dealing with attractive children (Adams and La-Voie, '75). It also appears that female—but not male—caregivers are prone toward more extensive use of punishment with unattractive boys than their attractive same-sex peers in a learning situation (Dion, '74). It should be noted, however, that in the Dion study, punishment was not defined as the administration of an aversive stimuli (such as a beating) but rather the removal of a positive reinforcer (money). Another investigation by Dion ('72), examining the influences of physical attractiveness on the socialization process, summarizes the full impact of what has been briefly examined here. College students were placed in a maternal role and asked to judge a child's personal character following a severe transgression of an established rule. Physically attractive children were viewed as just having an off-day, while unattractive children were judged as having deep-seeded antisocial personalities. From the conclusions drawn in these investigations, one can not help but wonder if mother love can actually overcome the psychological "obstacle" of having an unattractive child. A similar question would arise if we were looking at the effects of physical disability and handicappedness on parental behavior (Richardson, '76).

Educational Experience

As children mature they leave home for portions of the day to go to school. Thus, teachers become important caregivers. Consistent with parental behavior, teachers are also susceptible to making physical attractiveness stereotype-related attributions and expectations for children's behavior (Clifford and Walster, '73; Adams and Cohen, '74; Kehle *et al.*, '74; La Voie and Adams, '74; Adams and La Voie, '75; Adams, '78). Little is known about the degree to which teachers translate these stereotypic expectations into teacher-student interactions. In one observational study of classroom interactions (Adams and Cohen, '74), teacher-student interactions in a kindergarten and fourth and seventh grade classrooms were compared. Once interactions were observed, pictures of each child were judged for degree of physical attractiveness. Attractive children were then compared with unattractive children on the interaction measures. The major conclusion was that facial attractiveness was observed to be an increasingly useful predictor of teacher-student interactions with age. That is, the differences between attractive and unattractive children in the quality of teacher-student interactions did not emerge until the seventh grade. At that grade level, teacher-student interactions were observed to follow a physical attractiveness stereotype, with attractive children receiving more positive and frequent teacher involvement. Other, less direct evidence is available to support this conclusion. For example, in an examination of special needs programs for children, Barocas and Black ('74) found that attractive children were more readily identified and referred for additional educational assistance than unattractive children. It seems that teachers, like parents, are influenced by physical appearance. Facial attractiveness may not just mean positive teacher expectations, but translated into classroom behavior, it may also mean a more positive and attentive educational experience for attractive children.

Peer Relations

Peers are thought, in much of child development theory, to be extremely important contributors to individual growth and development. We might hope that early friendships and social relations are removed from assessments of an individual's physical characteristics, but are they? When examining the available literature, it becomes clear that, similar to parents and teachers, peers are influenced by physical appearance factors. Facial and body perceptions influence children's and adults' assessments of their peers' likeability and desirability as friends and playmates.

Evidence gathered from studies with children (Dion, '73; Dion and Berscheid, '74; Langlois and Stephan, '77; Adams and Crane, '80), young adults (Horai *et al.*, '74) and the elderly (Adams and Huston, '75) support the notion that peers are influenced by physical appearance factors. Further, body type research suggests that less attractive children, such as endomorphic, chubby children, experience a more distant interpersonal environment when interacting with peers (Lerner, '69; Lerner, '72; Lerner and Korn, '72; Lerner *et al.*, '76). Clearly, during the elementary school age years, initial contacts are influenced by attractiveness assessments. Kleck and co-workers ('74) have shown that popularity ratings and friendship choices following two weeks of camp are highly influenced by peer evaluations of attractiveness. Yet, it remains unclear when physical attractiveness becomes a primary determinant of peer relations. The data from the Kleck study cited above provide evidence that physical attractiveness stereotype expectations are translated into social relation patterns by the latter portion of the elementary school years. However, a recent investigation (Adams and Crane, '80) involving a child development preschool program suggests facial attractiveness may not be as widely influential for preschool age children. This is not to imply that the stereotype is non-existent at this young age. It merely means it is less pervasive. In two related studies, using photographs of attractive and unattractive children and adults, preschool children were asked to indicate (a) which person was most likely to be the nicer individual, and (b) if given a choice, which person they would most like to play with. Consistently, children judged the attractive person to be nicer, but showed no differences in their play choices. Thus, attractiveness influences in peer relations may emerge slowly, perhaps reaching its asymptote in influence during adolescence and young adulthood.

What actually occurs during social involvement with an attractive or unattractive peer? Data generated using both children (Dion, '77) and adults (Fugita *et al.*, '77) as subjects show that attractiveness functions as a reinforcing incentive for interpersonal attention. That is, when given the opportunity to view attractive and unattractive individuals, beautiful persons are given more visual attention. Further evidence suggests that during an interaction sequence with an attractive person, additional interpersonal processes emerge. Kleck and Rubenstein ('75), in an interview study where subjects interacted with an unattractive or attractive female, found that attractive women elicited more smiling and visual attention from their male interviewer. Also, several days later, the male subjects reported having thought more about the attractive female interviewer, remembering more about her appearance and indicating more liking for her than did male subjects who interacted with an unattractive female interviewer.

Attractiveness has other influential effects upon social exchange. For example, when in need, attractive individuals receive more assistance (Athanasious and Green, '73; Mims *et al.*, '75; West and Hodge, '75; Benson *et al.*, '76), are more readily cooperated with in conflict situations (Kahn *et al.*, '71; Sigall *et al*, '71), and experience more interpersonal information through self-disclosure with their associates (Cash and Soloway, '75; Brundage *et al.*, 77; Shea and Adams, '79). However, these effects of attractiveness may be mediated by certain social factors.

Two investigations demonstrate the mediational process which can negate direct effects of attractiveness upon interpersonal exchange. Sigall and Aronson ('69) examined the effects of attractiveness on liking for an individual when positive and negative evaluations are included as part of the social exchange. Attractive and unattractive female confederates provided either positive or negative evaluations to male research subjects prior to the subjects' completion of interpersonal assessments of the evaluators. Of the 4 groups (attractive females giving positive evaluations, unattractive females giving positive evaluations, etc.) the best-liked group was that of attractive women whose evaluations of the subject were positive, and the least-liked group was that of attractive women whose evaluations were negative. Unattractive women fell in the middle but were liked more when their evaluations were positive than negative. While attractive women may generally be more desirable, when these same women are critical they become least preferred—even less preferred than unattractive females who deliver negative evaluations.

Are these results translated into actual social behavior? To assess the mediational effects of interpersonal warmth (responsiveness) upon physical attractiveness stereotype effects in a social exchange situation, LaVoie and Adams ('78) designed an imitation study with adults. Recognizing that attractive individuals can exert social influence, it was hypothesized that, in an imitation learning experiment, attractive subjects were more likely to be imitated than unattractive subjects. However, interpersonal warmth and responsiveness have also been shown to be important determinants of imitation behavior. Therefore, male and female research subjects were randomly paired with either an attractive or unattractive male or female model who, depending upon the experimental condition, interacted with the subject in either a warm and responsive or in a cold and removed manner. While there was a tendency to imitate the attractive over unattractive model, warmth was the primary determinant of imitation. Thus, interpersonal warmth, kindness and responsiveness may mediate the social interactional effects of physical attractiveness.

Finally, while beauty has important effects upon reported liking of individuals, with respect to certain nonverbal communication and verbal behaviors it is important to recognize that in some interpersonal contexts, beauty may actually be perceived as unapproachable. In research investigating social interaction between bypassers on the street, it was observed that pedestrians maintain a greater distance between themselves and attractive persons versus unattractive persons (Dabbs and Stokes, '75; Powell and Dabbs, '76). Thus, within certain public contexts beauty may be seen as good but also unapproachable. However, whether pedestrian behavior parallels other social contexts is unclear. Thus, it is possible that these findings merely mean attractive persons do not have to mingle with the masses, tripping over others' feet and smelling others' body odor.

Dating and Mating

During adolescence and young adulthood, dating becomes a frequent and important behavior. Assuming that dating experiences are important prerequisites to effective mate selection, an understanding of the potential impact of physical attractiveness on the courtship process may be informative. Courtship literature has suggested that a variety of factors are important in mate selection. However, until recently, the effects of physical attractiveness upon the mate selection process have not been generally established through scientific methodology.

Extensive reviews of the effects of physical attractiveness on heterosexual involvement have been provided elsewhere (Berscheid and Walster, '74; Adams, '77; Adams and Crossman, '78). For specific details of this research, interested readers should consider these sources. In overview, this literature provides documented evidence for several important effects

33

which facial attractiveness may have on dating behavior. First, several investigations indicate that the physical attractiveness stereotype can have a strong influence upon dating preferences (Walster *et al.*, '66; Brislin and Lewis, '68; Bryne *et al.*, '70; Berscheid *et al.*, '71; Murstein, '72; Shepherd and Ellis, '72; Curran, '73; Huston, '73; Curran and Lippold, '75). Second, physical attractiveness, as an elicitor of physiological arousal, is influential in stimulating perceived sex appeal (Cavior *et al.*, '74) and sensations of love and emotional arousal (Critelli, '75; Peplau, '76; Shea and Adams, '79). Third, being associated with an attractive person has elevating effects upon an individual's perceived social desirability (Sigall and Landy, '73; Bar-Tal and Saxe, '74). Finally, physical attractiveness may have influential effects on sexual gratification and activity (Curran and Lippold, '75; MacCorquodale and Delamater, '79), and possibly on marital adjustment (Murstein and Christy, '76) and social prestige obtained through marital relationships (Elder, '69; Taylor and Glenn, '76; Udry, '77).

Most of the early work on the effects of physical attractiveness focused upon what has been called the matching hypothesis. Simply put, this hypothesis states that men and women of comparable social desirability will selectively seek each other out for dating and, ultimately, mating purposes. Thus, attractive men would pursue attractive women, unattractive men would date and mate unattractive women, etc. However, Walster and colleagues ('66), in three classic studies, failed to find support for such a hypothesis. Their conclusions were that attractive men and women were liked best, regardless of their personality characteristics. Berscheid and co-workers ('71) later argued that in this earlier investigation the saliency of possible rejection in the dating situation was unclear, and hence the conclusion of the study was not complete. Berscheid and colleagues attempted to correct this design limitation and engaged in yet another study to reassess the effects of physical appearance upon dating preference. Their conclusion, however, merely confirmed that physically attractive persons are preferred in a dating context and that the matching hypothesis, while being a social ideal, may not reflect social reality.

Further evidence suggests that while physically attractive persons are ideally preferred, there are social contexts where less attractive individuals have opportunities for dating experiences. Unsure of the research design employed in the previous research, Huston ('73) completed an investigation in which males were left in a state of ambiguity regarding their potential acceptability as a desirable dating choice of the sample of eligible females whose facial features were considered either attractive or unattractive. While attractive women may have remained the ideal preference, under social conditions which approach normal possibilities, Huston found that male subjects were likely to view their offer of a date as less acceptable to attractive females than to unattractive women. Once again, this suggests beauty may be viewed as good but unapproachable.

Is it possible that the effects of physical attractiveness may be minimized over time as two individuals in the course of dating come to know more about each other's personal characteristics? While such a possibility seems plausible, at least one investigation suggests it is not probable (Mathes, '75). In a controlled investigation which studied the effects of physical attractiveness upon liking over five dating encounters, Mathes failed to find a diminishing effect of physical attractiveness upon interpersonal desirability. Can this conclusion concerning dating relationships be generalized to include marriage relationships? While the data are limited, I believe it is reasonably safe to say that the final selection of a marriage partner is influenced by physical attractiveness. At least four studies suggest that the homogamy principle (*i.e.*, attractive individuals will marry attractive mates, etc.) can be confirmed from observational data gathered on married couples (Cavior and Boblett, '72; Murstein, '72; Shepherd and Ellis, '72; Murstein and Christy, '76). Thus, the influence of physical attractiveness not only is apparent in dating contexts but extends into marriage itself. Therefore, the data reviewed above suggest that attractive individuals are likely to have more potential for dates than unattractive persons, have more choices for marital partners and may be more able to marry attractive, high status mates.

Vocational Experience

Social involvement and interpersonal success on the job might be seen as removed from physical attractiveness influences, yet some data might be drawn upon to argue the contrary. While it would be hard to argue that qualifications are unimportant, it is equally difficult to suggest that attractiveness plays no role in obtaining employment. Two investigations on the effects of attractiveness upon hiring decisions (Dipboye *et al.*, '75; Cash *et al.*, '77) have shown that personnel decisions are influenced by attractiveness, with physically attractive applicants more likely than less attractive applicants to receive an employment offer, given equal qualifications. Indications are that when hired, attractive persons would also be viewed as more effective than unattractive persons when performance is actually poor (Landy and Sigall, '74) and given more credit than an unattractive person when successful (Seligman *et al.*, '73). Thus, attractiveness may well have social interaction influences in employment settings.

Legal Experiences

Although some have argued that justice is blind, I believe most of us like to believe in a *just world hypothesis*. That is, justice will prevail and each of us will receive our just due. However, is it possible that juries are swayed by beauty? Some evidence suggests that facial attractiveness may well have an effect upon the outcome of legal action (Monohan, '41; Efran, '74). Like Dion's ('74) research which suggests attractive children may receive less punishment than unattractive children for social transgressions, mock jury research suggests unattractive individuals may receive larger jail sentences than attractive defendants. Conversely, other evidence suggests that when a mock jury is convinced that an attractive person has abused his natural gift of beauty and used it to illegally obtain material goods, this desirable physical attribute may well become a liability rather than an asset. For example, Sigall and Ostrove ('75), in a simulated jury study, examined the relationship between attractiveness and type of crime upon jury decision making. College students acting as jury members were presented with legal cases in which an individual was reported to have been caught engaging in either a swindle (con game) or a burglary (nonviolent). The results of the jury decisions were quite interesting. When attractive and unattractive defendants were found guilty of a swindle, the attractive person was given a longer sentence than the unattractive person. However, when the defendants were found guilty of burglary, the unattractive person received a much longer jail sentence than an attractive person.

Could it also be that attractiveness plays a role in understanding how victims of crime are perceived? Could it be that attractive persons are less stigmatized due to victimization, or is it possible that they are given more blame for being victimized than unattractive individuals? Perhaps the ideal test of these questions might be directed to the case of rape, where victims are many times blamed for being victimized. In a recent investigation of the effects of attractiveness on attributions of blame for rape, Baunach ('74) has shown that attractive victims are perceived as responsible for their rape experience. However, the degree of attractiveness of the individual making such judgments was observed to be particularly important. In the case of unattractive research subjects who were asked to make attributions of responsibility, it was observed that attractive rather than unattractive victims were judged as being more contributive to their being victimized. Thus, attractive persons may be viewed as responsible for their victimization and be given attributions of contribution for victimization, when in reality they had no contributive role at all.

Mental Health Assistance

With increasing frequency, children and adults turn to mental health professionals for assistance. Is it possible that mental health counselors are also influenced by the physical attributes of their clients? An investigation by Barocas and Vance ('74) sought to determine if professional counselors were influenced by attractiveness in their prognosis of recovery for their college student clients. Each client's degree of attractiveness was assessed by a secretary prior to being seen by a counselor. At the close of the session, each counselor gave a prognosis evaluation. The conclusion was that attractive clients were predicted to have more rapid recovery than their unattractive counterparts. There is yet another side of this coin. Another investigation (Shapiro *et al.*, '76) showed that clients (patients) view attractive therapists as more competent and have been demonstrated to show more positive improvement under their treatment. Finally, while unattractive individuals are viewed as less healthy and are more likely to be referred for psychiatric hospitalization, some evidence also suggests attractiveness may work against the attractive person. Cash and colleagues, (Cash *et al.*, '77) showed that when attractive individuals have extensive psychological problems, therapists are inclined to view their patients' problems as less serious than they really are and may give less attention than is actually required. One might speculate that therapists assume the peer relations of the attractive individual are so supportive that a natural remission of the psychological disturbance will occur; that it will correct itself through normal social interaction, which perhaps it may just do.

PERSONALITY DEVELOPMENT

Thus far, the research literature has shown that the physical attractiveness stereotype functions according to a beauty-is-good hypothesis with noted exceptions when beauty may fail. Further, data have been reviewed which indicate that attractive individuals generally experience a positive social milieu, while unattractive persons are socialized in a neutral to negative social environment. It has also been shown that parents, peers, teachers, employers and others are prone to interacting with attractive and unattractive persons according to the stereotypic expectations outlined earlier. Does this process go even further? Is there evidence to suggest that attractive and unattractive individuals actually internalize stereotypic expectations in their personality formation?

Recently, Snyder and colleagues ('77) proposed that "social stereotypes may create their own social reality by channeling social interaction in ways that cause stereotyped individuals to behaviorally confirm the perceiver's stereotype." In sociological circles, a popular theory has been proposed to explain this process. Symbolic interaction theory proposes that the concept of self evolves from social exchange through a process of interaction between role expectations and role performance with personal reference groups. In other words, the other can serve the role of a looking glass in which one sees oneself as a kind of object and the self develops out of others' appraisals, feedback and expectations (For an extensive review of the social psychological literature supporting behavioral confirmation of stereotypes, see Snyder, in press).

To test the potential self-fulfilling nature of a physical attractiveness stereotype, Snyder and co-workers ('77) devised an ingenious investigation where males carried on a telephone conversation with females who were reported to be either attractive or unattractive. The females were unaware of this previous labeling process and were lead to believe they were merely completing a brief communication task. Further, the women were randomly identified to the males as either attractive or unattractive. Thus, both the attractive and unattractive groups had a random assortment of women with various degrees of attractiveness. Using both the telephone conversation and questionnaire data following the communication task, the investigators examined the data for evidence of behavioral confirmation of the physical attractiveness stereotype. The male research subjects expected their attractive conversation partners to act in a poised, sociable manner, to be humorous and generally to be interpersonally adept. Unattractive conversational partners were anticipated to be serious, awkward and inept. Analysis of the telephone conversation data found that women who were labeled attractive (unannounced to them) manifested greater animation, confidence and interpersonal adeptness than women labeled as unattractive to the male subjects. As Snyder remarked, "What had initially been reality in the minds of the men had now become reality in the behavior of the women with whom they had interacted." Thus, experimental data can be found to suggest that social impressions can influence social interaction in a way which can channel an individual's personality characteristics and social behavior.

Other personality research can be drawn upon to support the assumption that physical attractiveness can channel social behavior into a confirmatory process. The general assumption of the beauty-is-good hypothesis is that attractiveness is associated with socially desirable attributes. If the stereotype, through social channeling influences, leads to behavioral confirmation, then evidence should be found to show that attractive persons possess more desirable personality traits than their unattractive counterpart. Generally speaking, personality research can be viewed as supporting such an assumption. Facial attractiveness has been shown to be associated with a positive self-concept (Lerner *et al.*, '73; Lerner and Karabenick, '74; Adams, '77), sensation-seeking tendencies (Adams, '77*b*; Adams, '79), independence or inquisitiveness (Krebs and Adinolfi, '75; Adams, '77*b*; Lerner and Lerner, '77; Salvai *et al.*, '77), and positive mental health (Kahn, '75; Lerner and Lerner, '77; Adams, '79).

In one particular investigation (Adams, '79), an attempt was made to move beyond the usual sample of college students to a sample of working men and women in order to assess the proposed differences in personalities for attractive and unattractive individuals. A random sample of 301 men and women was drawn from five towns which collectively represented just under 75,000 inhabitants. Individuals between the ages of 18 and 80 years of age were assessed on physical attractiveness, personality and social interaction measures. Little confirmation of the proposed relationship between the attractiveness stereotype and personality could be confirmed for the male sample. A much different picture emerged for the women. Attractive women, when contrasted with their unattractive counterparts, were found to be more self-accepting of themselves, perceived themselves as more likeable, saw themselves as being in control of their own destiny and appeared less fearful of negative evaluations from others, regardless of age. Further evidence suggested that attractive women in this sample also had more social involvement and interaction with others.

It can safely be concluded that attractiveness can have channeling effects so that personality characteristics may emerge which reinforce the stereotype. However, this may be more likely for women than men.

SOCIAL BEHAVIOR

The evidence just reviewed suggests that stereotypic channeling effects can have an influence upon personality. Further, the last study reviewed in the previous section indicates that attractive persons (women, at least) manifest these differential personality traits in their social behavior. Several additional studies confirm this conclusion. For example, Jackson and Huston ('75) have shown that attractive women are more assertive than their unattractive peers when faced with impolite behavior. However, Dion and Stein ('78) and Langlois and Downs ('79) have reported unattractive children may be more assertive and aggressive than their attractive peers. Further, due to their positive self concepts, attractive men and women are more able to resist peer pressure influences (Adams, '77b) and maintain their own perspective. Other evidence suggests attractive individuals may be more socially skilled than their unattractive counterparts (Goldman and Lewis, '77).

Given that attractive individuals have more total reinforcing social experiences over their life course (Cash and Burns, '77; Adams, '79) and that the physical attractiveness stereotype assumes attractive individuals are successful and powerful individuals, beauty should be associated with unique interpersonal influence styles. Two investigations, one with children and the other with adults, demonstrate this assumption. For example, Dion and Stein ('78), using fifth and sixth graders as subjects, offered a monetary incentive for demonstrating persuasiveness with same-aged peers. To assess manipulative social influence, the effects of attractive and unattractive boys and girls in persuading a peer to eat an unpleasant tasting (but harmless) cracker were compared to an appropriate control group. The unattractive boys were more successful with male than female peers while attractive boys and girls were most influential with opposite sex peers. Further, unique persuasion styles were noted. Unattractive males mostly used threat and commands to influence their peers. Attractive males were persistently assertive but not aggressive. These males coaxed, reassured and pleaded. Such tactics were not influential with males but did have successful persuasion effects with female peers. Unattractive girls were assertive but not particularly successful. Attractive girls were quite successful with opposite-sex peers but were likely to exhibit very few persuasion attempts and were reportedly judged to be the least persistent and forceful of the four attractiveness groups. Thus, children of varying degrees of attractiveness appear to use persuasion styles which are differentially effective in influencing peers but are reasonably consistent with a physical attractiveness stereotype. In another investigation using adult subjects, Chaiken ('79) examined the effects of men's and women's persuasive efforts on same and opposite-sex peers' willingness to sign a petition. Regardless of the sex of the communicator or of the individuals approached for signatures, attractive communicators were able to acquire more agreement to the content of the petition than were unattractive communicators. Further, more individuals actually signed the petition for the attractive communicators. Follow-up data indicated that attractive communicators were viewed as somewhat more friendly than their unattractive counterparts, with additional evidence suggesting that attractive persons were more verbally fluent, spoke at a somewhat faster rate and regarded themselves as more optimistic, interesting and persuasive.

In summary, these data are supportive of the overall theme of this chapter. That is, physical appearance conveys stereotypic impressions which imply social attributions focusing upon a beauty-is-good hypothesis. In turn, these attributions generate unique social experiences for attractive and unattractive persons. Due to the positive social milieu of the attractive person, they are likely to internalize a socially desirable personality profile, while some unattractive individuals are negatively influenced in their internalization of personality characteristics. Finally, these differential personality characteristics stimulate more socially influential and effective social interaction styles for attractive than for unattractive persons.

THE SOCIALIZATION OF THE PHYSICAL ATTRACTIVENESS STEREOTYPE

The assumption that physical attractiveness can have a powerful influence upon personality development and social behavior through a socialization process has been addressed; however, there is yet another socialization process to be examined. Where does the stereotype originate? Who are the transmission agents of this stereotype? That is, who actually socializes children into using or believing in the attractiveness stereotype?

While it is unclear from whence the stereotype originates, it is evident that historians, philosophers, religious leaders and scientists alike have recognized the stereotype for centuries. Further, given that research literature suggests the overwhelming use of the stereotype across settings, occasions and social roles, it is likely that most of us help to instill the stereotype in young people. However, as a social scientist I have not been content with such a sweeping statement and have begun a research program to identify the primary contributors to this socialization process. Given that young children have two major types of caregivers, attention has initially been focused upon parents and preschool teachers as possible primary socialization agents of the physical attractiveness stereotype.

In a series of investigations (Adams and Crane, '80), an attempt has been made to determine the degree to which mothers, fathers or teachers, as primary caregivers, socialize young children with the beauty-is-good hypothesis. Using attractive and unattractive white and black boys and girls as the stimulus for interpersonal judgments, subjects were asked to indicate which child was the nicer individual and with whom they would most like to play. Further, fathers, mothers and preschool teachers of each child were asked how they *expected* their child to respond. Briefly, the results indicated that children viewed attractive children as more likely to be nice, but showed no play preference between attractive and unattractive children. However, parents and teachers expected their children to use a physical attractiveness stereotype in both their social attribution and play preference choices. Further analyses revealed that, in particular, mothers' and female preschool teachers' expectations had the closest association with the child's actual use of the stereotype. That is, mothers and teachers who expected their children to use the stereotype had children who were more likely to use it in their attribution and play preferences than mothers and teachers who held low expectations for such behavior. Expectations of fathers about their childrens' use of the stereotype had very little correlation with whether the child did or did not use the stereotype.

These data suggest that when female caregivers of young children hold a physical attractiveness stereotype, they may socialize children to use it through subtle reinforcement or self-fulfilling prophecy mechanisms. It is not unreasonable to suspect that similar findings might be found when future research studies the possible effects of siblings, grandparents, aunts and uncles. Also, it is at this point unclear how schooling and educational experiences, television viewing, reading, play activities with peers, etc., might contribute to this socialization process.

CONCLUSION

It would be difficult to conclude this chapter without a final comment on the broad implications of the substance of this chapter. Recognizing that physical attractiveness has powerful influences upon impressions *and* social behavior highlights the value of much which is accomplished by the field of medicine. In working with youth to assure maximal trends in somatic and physical development, practitioners in allied health fields are assisting their patients beyond physical well-being. Assisting individuals toward positive physical appearance not only provides an appealing body image but also promotes positive socialization experiences which support healthy personality development. Medical efforts can have effects far beyond the clinic.

REFERENCES

Adams, G. R. Physical attractiveness: Toward a developmental social psychology of beauty. Hum. Devel. *20*:217-239, 1977*a*.

Adams, G. R. Physical attractiveness, personality and social reactions to peer pressure. J. Psych. *96*:287-296, 1977*b*.

Adams, G. R. Racial membership and physical attractiveness effects on preschool teachers' expectations. Child Study J. *8*:29-41, 1978.

Adams, G. R. Beautiful is good: A test of the "kernel of truth" hypothesis. Submitted manuscript, 1979.

Adams, G. R. and A. S. Cohen. Children's physical and interpersonal characteristics that affect student-teacher interactions. J. Exper. Ed. *43*:1-5, 1974.

Adams, G. R. and P. Crane. An assessment of parents' and teachers' expectations of preschool children's social preference for attractive or unattractive children and adults. Child Devel. In press, 1980.

Adams, G. R. and S. M. Crossman. *Physical Attractiveness: A Cultural Imperative.* Libra Publishing, Rosyln Heights, N. Y., 1978.

Adams, G. R. and T. L. Huston. Social perception of middle-aged persons varying in physical attractiveness. Devel. Psych. *11*:656-658, 1975.

Adams, G. R. and J. C. LaVoie. The effects of sex of child, conduct and facial attractiveness on teacher expectancy. Educ. *95*:76-83, 1974.

Adams, G. R. and J. C. LaVoie. Parental expectations of educational and personal-social performance and childrearing patterns as a function of attractiveness, sex and conduct of the child. Child Study J. *5*:125-142, 1975.

Adams, G. R. and J. C. LaVoie. Teacher expectations: A review of the student characteristics used in expectancy formation. J. Instruct. Psych. Mono. *4*:1-28, 1977.

Athanasious, R. and P. Greene. Physical attractiveness and helping behavior. In: Proceedings of the 81st Annual American Psychological Association Convention, 1973.

Barocas, R. and F. L. Vance. Referral rate and physical attractiveness in third-grade children. Percept. Mot. Skills *39*:731-734, 1974.

Bar-Tal, D. and L. Saxe. Effect of physical attractiveness on the perception of couples. Paper presented at the American Psychological Association Convention, New Orleans, August, 1974.

Baunach, P. J. Physical attractiveness and attribution of victim responsibility for attractiveness-related and attractiveness-unrelated crimes: Who blames beauty and when? Doctoral dissertation, University of Minnesota, 1974.

Benson, P. L., S. A. Karabenick and R. M. Lerner. Pretty pleases: The effects of physical attractiveness, race and sex on receiving help. J. Exper. Soc. Psych. *12*:409-415, 1976.

Berscheid, E., K. Dion, E. Walster and G. W. Walster. Physical attractiveness and dating choice: A test of the matching hypothesis. J. Exper. Soc. Psych. *7*:173-180, 1971.

Berscheid, E. and E. Walster. Physical attractiveness. In: *Advances in Experimental Social Psychology*, Vol. 7. L. Berkowitz (ed.). Academic Press, New York, 1974.

Boukydis, Z. C. Infant attractiveness and the infant- caretaker relationship. Paper presented at the International Conference on Love and Attraction, University College of Swansea, Wales, U.K., September, 1977.

Brislin, R. W. and S. A. Lewis. Dating and physical attractiveness: Replication. Psych. Rep. *22*:976, 1968.

Brundage, L. E., V. J. Derlega and T. F. Cash. The effects of physical attractiveness and need for approval on self-disclosure. Person. Soc. Psych. Bull. *3*:63-66, 1977.

Bryne, D., C. Ervin and J. Lamberth. Continuity between the experimental study of attraction and real-life computer dating. J. Person. Soc. Psych. *16*:157-165, 1970.

Cash, T. F. and P. J. Begley. Internal-external control, achievement orientation and physical attractiveness of college students. Psych. Rep. *38*:1205-1206, 1976.

Cash, T. F. and D. S. Burns. The occurrence of reinforcing activities in relation to locus of control, success-failure expectancies and physical attractiveness. J. Person. Assess. *41*:387-391, 1977.

Cash, T. F., B. Gillen and D. S. Burns. Sexism and "beautyism" in personal consultant decision making. J. Appl. Psych. *62*:301-310, 1977.

Cash, T. F., J. Kehr, J. Polyson and V. Freeman. Role of physical attractiveness in peer attribution of psychological disturbance. J. Consult. Clin. Psych. *45*:987-993, 1977.

Cash, T. F. and D. Soloway. Self-disclosure correlates of physical attractiveness: An exploratory study. Psych. Rep. *36*:579-586, 1975.

Cavior, N. and P. J. Boblett. Physical attractiveness of dating versus married couples. In: Proceedings of the 80th Annual Convention, American Psychological Association, 1972.

Cavior, N., A. Jacobs and M. Jacobs. The stability and correlation of physical attractiveness and sex appeal ratings. Unpublished manuscript, West Virginia University, Morgantown, W.V., 1974.

Cavior, N. and D. A. Lombardi. Developmental aspects of judgment of physical attractiveness in children. Devel. Psych. *8*:67-71, 1973.

Chaiken, S. Communicator physical attractiveness and persuasion. J. Person. Soc. Psych. *37*:1387-1397, 1979.

Clifford, M. and E. Walster. The effect of physical attractiveness on teacher expectations. Soc. Ed. *46*:248-258, 1973.

Corter, C., S. Trehub, C. Boukydis, L. Ford, L. Clehoffer and K. Minde. Nurses' judgments of the attractivness of premature infants. Infant Behav. and Devel. *1*:373-380, 1978.

Critelli, J. W. Physical attractiveness in dating couples. Paper presented at the Annual Meeting of the American Psychological Association, September, 1975.

Cross, J. F. and J. Cross. Age, sex, race and the perception of facial beauty. Devel. Psych. *5*:433-439, 1971.

Curran, J. P. Correlates of physical attractiveness and interpersonal attraction in the dating situation. Soc. Beh. Person. *1*:153-157, 1973.

Curran, J. P. and S. Lippold. The effects of physical attraction and attitude similarity on attraction in dating dyads. J. Person. *43*:528-539, 1975.

Dabbs, J. M. and N. A. Stokes. Beauty is power: The use of space in the sidewalk. Sociometry *38*:551-557, 1975.

Dermer, M. and D. L. Thiel. When beauty may fail. J. Person. Soc. Psych. *31*:1168-1176, 1975.

Dion, K. K. Young children's stereotyping of facial attractiveness. Devel. Psych. *9*:183-188, 1973.

Dion, K. K. Children's physical attractiveness and sex as determinants of adult punitiveness. Devel. Psych. *10*:772-778, 1974.

Dion, K. K. The incentive value of physical attractiveness for young children. Person. Soc. Psych. Bull. *3*:67-70, 1977.

Dion, K. K. and E. Berscheid. Physical attractiveness and peer perception among children. Sociometry *37*:1-12, 1974.

Dion, K., E. Berscheid and E. Walster. What is beautiful is good. J. Person. Soc. Psych. *24*:285-290, 1972.

Dion, K. K. and S. Stein. Physical attractiveness and interpersonal influence. J. Exper. Soc. Psych. *14*:97-108, 1978.

Dipboye, R. L., H. L. Fromkin and K. Wiback. Relative importance of applicant sex, attractiveness and scholastic standing in evaluation of job applicant resumes. J. Appl. Psych. *60*:39-43, 1975.

Efran, M. G. The effect of physical appearance on the judgment of guilt, interpersonal attraction and severity of recommended punishment in a simulated jury task. J. Res. Person. *8*:45-54, 1974.

Eibl-Eibesfeldt, I. *Ethology*. Holt, Rinehart and Winston, New York, 1970.

Elder, G. H. Appearance and education in marriage mobility. Am. Sociol. Rev. *34*:519-533, 1969.

Fugita, S. S., T. A. Agle, I. Newman and N. Walfish. Attractiveness, self-concept and a methodological note about gaze behavior. Person. Soc. Psych. Bull. *3*:240-243, 1977.

Goldman, W. and P. Lewis. Beautiful is good: Evidence that the physically attractive are more socially skillful. J. Exper. Soc. Psych. *13*:125-130, 1977.

Hildebrandt, K. A. Adult responses to infant cuteness. Unpublished master's thesis. Michigan State University, East Lansing, Michigan, 1976.

Hildebrandt, K. A. and H. E. Fitzgerald. Gender bias in observers' perception of infants sex: Boy most of the time. Percept. Motor Skills *45*:472-474, 1977.

Hill, M. K. and H. A. Lando. Physical attractiveness and sex-role stereotypes in impression formation. Percept. Motor Skills *43*:1251-1255, 1976.

Horai, J., N. Naccari and E. Fatoullah. The effects of expertise and physical attractiveness upon opinion agreement and liking. Sociometry *37*:601-606, 1974.

Huston, T. L. Ambiguity of acceptance, social desirability and dating choice. J. Exper. Soc. Psych. *9*:32-42, 1973.

Jackson, D. and T. L. Huston. Physical attractiveness and assertiveness. J. Soc. Psych. *96*:79-84, 1975.

Kahn, A., J. Hottes and W. L. Davis. Cooperation and optimal responding in the prisoner's dilemma game: Effects of sex and physical attractiveness. J. Person. Soc. Psych. *17*:267-279, 1971.

Kehle, T. J., W. J. Bramble and J. Mason. Teachers' expectations: Rating of student performance as biased by student characteristics. J. Exper. Ed. *43*:54-60, 1974.

Kleck, R. E., S. A. Richardson and L. Ronald. Physical appearance cues and interpersonal attraction in children. Child Devel. *45*:305-310, 1974.

Kleck, R. E. and C. Rubenstein. Physical attractiveness, perceived attitude similarity and interpersonal attraction in an opposite-sex encounter. J. Person. Soc. Psych. *31*:107-114, 1975.

Krebs, D. and A. A. Adinolfi. Physical attractiveness, social relations and personality style. J. Person. Soc. Psych. *31*:245-253, 1975.

Landy, D. and H. Sigall. Beauty is talent: Task evaluation as a function of the performer's physical attractiveness. J. Person. Soc. Psych. *29*:299-304, 1974.

Landy, D. and H. Sigall. Beauty is talent: Task evaluation as a function of the performer's physical attractiveness. J. Person. Soc. Psych. *29*:299-304, 1974.

Langlois, J. H. and A. C. Downs. Peer relations as a function of physical attractiveness: The eye of the beholder or behavior reality. Child Devel. *50*:409-418, 1979.

Langlois, J. H. and C. Stephan. The effects of physical attractiveness and ethnicity on children's behavioral attributions and peer preferences. Child Devel. *48*:1694-1698, 1977.

LaVoie, J. C. and G. R. Adams. Teacher expectancy and its relation to physical and interpersonal characteristics of the child. Alberta J. Ed. Res. *22*:122-132, 1974.

Lerner, R. M. The development of stereotyped expectancies of body build-behavior relations. Child Devel. *40*:137-141, 1969.

Lerner, R. M. Richness analyses of body build stereotype development. Devel. Psych. 7:219, 1972.

Lerner, R. M., S. Isawki and T. Chihara. Development of personal space schemata among Japanese children. Devel. Psych. *12*:466-467, 1976.

Lerner, R. M. and S. A. Karabenick. Physical attractiveness, body attitudes and self-concept in late adolescents. J. Youth Adol. *3*:307-316, 1974.

Lerner, R. M., S. A. Karabenick and J. L. Stuart. Relations among physical attractiveness, body attitudes and self-concept in male and female college students. J. Psych. *85*:119-129, 1973.

Lerner, R. M. and S. J. Korn. The development of body build stereotypes in males. Child Devel. *43*:908-920, 1972.

Lerner, R. M. and J. V. Lerner. Effects of age, sex and physical attractiveness on child-peer relations, academic performance and elementary school adjustment. Devel. Psych. *13*:585-590, 1977.

Lorenz, K. Die angeborenen Formen moglicher Erfahrung. Zeit. fur Tierpsych., pp. 245-409, 1943.

Lucker, G. W., W. E. Beane and R. Helmreich. Exploring the eye of the beholder: Attractiveness and attributions. J. Psychol. In press.

MacCorquodale, P. and J. Delamater. Self-image and premarital sexuality. J. Marr. Fam. *41*:327-339, 1979.

Mathes, E. W. The effects of physical attractiveness and anxiety on heterosexual attraction over a series of five encounters. J. Marr. Fam. *37*:769-774, 1975.

Mathes, E. W. and A. Kahn. Physical attractiveness, happiness, neuroticism and self-esteem. J. Psych. *90*:27-30, 1975.

McKelvie, S. J. and S. J. Matthews. Effects of physical attractiveness and favorableness of character on liking. Psych. Rep. *38*:1223-1230, 1976.

Miller, A. G. Role of physical attractiveness in impression formation. Psychonomic Sci. *19*:241-243, 1970*a*.

Miller, A. G. Social perception of internal-external control. Percept. Mot. Skills *30*:103-109, 1970*b*.

Mims, P. R., J. J. Hartnett and W. R. Nay. Interpersonal attraction and help volunteering as a function of physical attractiveness. J. Psych. *89*:125-131, 1975.

Monahan, F. *Women in Crime*. Washburn, New York , 1941.

Murstein, B. I. Physical attractiveness and marital choice. J. Person. Soc. Psych. *22*:8-12, 1972.

Murstein, B. I. and P. Christy. Physical attractiveness and marriage adjustment in middle-aged couples. J. Person. Soc. Psych. *34*:537-542, 1976.

Peplau, L. A. Sex, love and the double standard. Paper presented at the meetings of the American Psychological Association, Washington, 1976.

Powell, P. H. and J. M. Dabbs. Physical attractiveness and personal space. J. Soc. Psych. *100*:59-64, 1976.

Richardson, S. A. Attitudes and behavior toward the physically handicapped. Birth Defects: Original Articles Series *12*:15-34, 1976.

Salvie, J., R. Algozzine and J. B. Sheare. Attractiveness and school achievement. J. School Psych. *15*:60-67, 1977.

Schneider, D. J. Implicit personality theory: A review. Psych. Bull. *79*:294-309, 1973.

Seligman, C. N., N. Pascall and G. Takata. Attribution of responsibility for a chance event as a function of physical attractiveness of target person, outcome and likelihood of event. Paper presented at the meetings of the American Psychological Association, Montreal, 1973.

Shapiro, A. K., E. Struening, E. Shapiro and H. Barten. Prognostic correlates of psychotherapy in psychiatric outpatients. Am. J. Psychiatry *133*:802-808, 1976.

Shea, J. A. and G. R. Adams. Correlates of male and female romantic attachments: A path analysis study. Submitted for publication, 1979.

Shepherd, J. W. and H. D. Ellis. Physical attractiveness and selection of marriage partners. Psych. Rep. *30*:1004, 1972.

Sigall, H. and E. Aronson. Liking for an evaluator as a function of her physical attractiveness and nature of the evaluations. J. Exper. Soc. Psych. *5*:93-100, 1969.

Sigall, H. and D. Landy. Radiating beauty: The effects of having a physically attractive partner on person perception. J. Person. Soc. Psych. *28*:218-224, 1973.

Sigall, H. and N. Ostrove. Beautiful but dangerous: Effects of offender attractiveness and nature of the crime in juridic judgment. J. Person. Soc. Psych. *31*:410-414, 1975.

Sigall, H., R. Page and A. C. Brown. Effort expenditure as a function of evaluation and evaluator attractiveness. Repr. Res. Soc. Psych. *2*:19-25, 1971.

Snyder, M. On the self-perpetuating nature of social stereotypes. In: *Cognitive Process in Stereotyping and Intergroup Behavior*, P. L. Hamilton (ed.), Erblaum, Hillsdale, New Jersey, in press.

Snyder, M., E. D. Tanke and E. Berscheid. Social perception and interpersonal behavior: On the self-fulfilling nature of social stereotypes. J. Person. Soc. Psych. *35*:656-666, 1977.

Taylor, P. A. and N. D. Glenn. The utility of education and attractiveness for females' status attainment through marriage. Am. Sociol. Rev. *41*:484-497, 1976.

Walster, E., V. Aronson, D. Abrahams and L. Rottmann. Importance of physical attractiveness in dating behavior. J. Person. Soc. Psych. *4*:508-516, 1966.

West, S. G. and P. G. Hodge. Physical attractiveness, blindness (dependency) and helping. Paper presented at the Southeastern Psychological Assn., 1975.

Wilson, M., T. F. Cash and S. G. West. Divergent effects of physical attractiveness on impression formation as a function of the situational context. Paper presented at the Eastern Psychological Association Convention, Washington, D.C., April, 1978.

Udry, J. R. The importance of being beautiful: A reexamination and racial comparison. Am. J. Sociol. *83*:154-160, 1977.

ESTHETICS AND A QUANTITATIVE ANALYSIS OF FACIAL APPEARANCE

G. William Lucker, Ph.D.

Center for Human Growth and Development
The University of Michigan

Until very recently, the study of facial esthetics has been primarily the province of painters, sculptors and philosophers. Beauty has been viewed as a subjective quality, defined by the eye of the beholder. However, the recently acquired ability to clinically intervene and change facial structure has necessitated the development of more objective esthetic standards. Norms for the size, shape, and interrelationship of facial structures have had to be developed in order to quantify the degree to which a patient deviates from the average and to decide the kind and degree of clinical intervention necessary to produce a normal appearance. Situations where normal facial structures are missing due to birth defects or catastrophe have required a knowledge not only of structural dimensions but also of precise location of those facial structures.

In the first section of this paper, some general criteria for quantifying facial esthetics taken primarily from the plastic and reconstructive surgery literature will be presented. Then some very precise techniques for the measurement of facial form taken primarily from the orthodontic and dental literature are presented, and, finally, research which has related these precise measurements to esthetic standards is discussed.

It should be noted at the outset that this presentation will be limited in several ways. First, only the esthetic relationship of static facial bones and soft tissue will be discussed. Facial expression, an equally important aspect of facial esthetics, is beyond the scope of this report. Second, the individual difference component of the perception of facial esthetics will not be discussed. Factors like an individual's self-concept, motivational state, past experience, and direction of attention can have profound effects on esthetic perceptions, but these variables will not be considered here. Finally, the esthetic standards that will be discussed are taken from American literature. Therefore, only American facial esthetic standards will be examined. These standards may be applicable elsewhere, but no claims about the universality of their applicability are made.

49

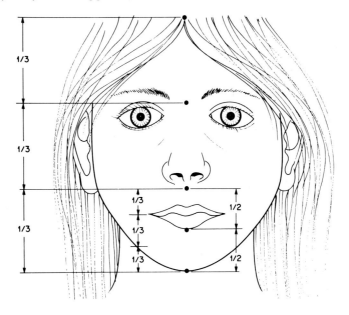

Figure 1. Vertical facial proportions from the frontal aspect. Note that the typical face should divide vertically into three equal parts.

FACIAL PROPORTION

The most fundamental consideration in facial esthetics is facial proportion. Contemporary standards for facial proportion can be traced back to the Greeks. More recently, Broadbent and Matthews ('57) and Patterson and Powell ('74) have compiled what they consider to be some of the most important proportional relations from the frontal view (Fig. 1). They report that if the face is divided vertically into three parts by horizontal lines through the hairline, glabella (or brow ridge), and chin, those segments should be approximately equal in height. If the lower third of the face is further subdivided, the upper and lower lip junction should be one-third the distance down from nose to chin, the vermilion border of the lower lip should be about one-half the distance down from nose to chin, and supramentale, the depression below the lower lip, should be about two-thirds the distance down from nose to chin.

Horizontally, the face should be symmetrical in size, form and arrangement of facial features. Balanced faces usually have the width of an eye between the eyes (Fig. 2). The width of the mouth should equal the distance between the inner borders of the iris on a direct forward gaze. The width of the nose should be approximately equal to the distance between the eyes.

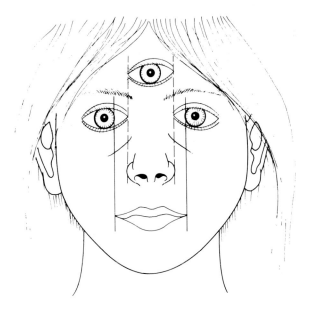

Figure 2. Horizontal facial proportions from the frontal aspect. Balanced faces usually have the width of an eye between the eyes, and the width of the mouth is usually equal to the distance between the linear borders of the iris.

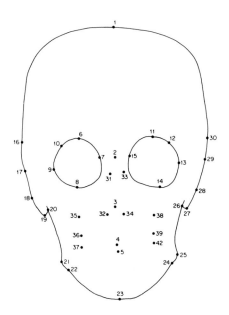

Figure 3. Cephalometric landmarks from the frontal aspect.

51

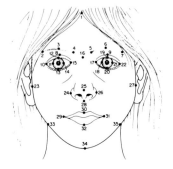

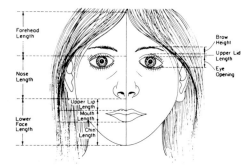

Figure 4. Soft tissue landmarks from the frontal aspect.

Figure 5. Soft tissue vertical measures from the frontal aspect.

Although the face is usually seen from a multitude of perspectives and angles, angular views and three-dimensional representations complicate precise measurement of the face. It has therefore become conventional to base facial feature analysis on full frontal and profile (side) representations of the face. In the following discussion, the measurements from the frontal and lateral aspects will be dealt with separately.

MEASUREMENT FROM THE FRONTAL ASPECT

Measurement from the frontal aspect will be dealt with first, not because it is the easiest and most completely defined set of measures, but because it is the least used and hardest to define set of measures. Although hard tissue landmarks were developed by physical anthropologists nearly one hundred years ago and presented more recently in the works of such people as Broadbent and Matthews ('57), Krogman and Sassouni ('57; Fig. 3), there is no unified compendium of measures based on these landmarks. These landmarks have generally been used to determine proportion, both vertical and horizontal, and left-right facial symmetry. Soft tissue landmarks (Fig. 4) have also been developed to approximate those made on hard tissue structures, and since they are easier to describe, measures of vertical and horizontal proportion and left-right symmetry are illustrated using soft tissue landmarks (Figs. 5–7). For example, two common vertical soft tissue measures are upper and lower face height

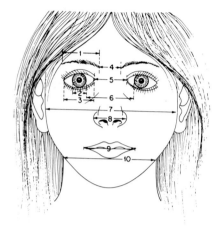

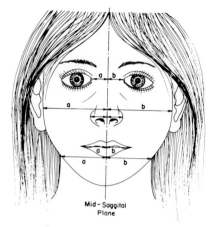

Figure 6. Soft tissue horizontal measures from the frontal aspect.

Figure 7. Soft tissue facial symmetry. Left-right symmetry is measured from the middle of the face to the left and right sides. Discrepancies between distances indicate degree of asymmetry.

(which are labeled here as nose length and lower face height; Fig. 5). Additional vertical soft tissue measures might include upper lip length, mouth length, and chin length, as well as brow height, upper eyelid length, and vertical eye opening. Two common horizontal measures are bizygomatic width (the breadth of the cheekbones) and bigonial width (the breadth of the lower jaw; Fig. 6). Additional horizontal soft tissue measures might include eyebrow length, iris width, eye length, distance between the eyebrows, distance between the eyes, distance between the irises, nose width, and mouth length.

To determine left-right symmetry, distances from landmarks to the middle of the face (mid-saggital plane) are measured from the left and right sides of the face (Fig. 7). Symmetry can be measured with regard to the eyes, cheekbones, nose, mouth and lower jaw. Discrepancies between distances indicate degree of facial asymmetry. Facial symmetry of soft tissue structures can most easily be determined using x-y coordinate grid overlays on frontal facial photographs (Fig. 8), or lucite overlays on the surface of the face.

Frontal facial esthetics has remained primarily the province of the practicing clinician, but there has been some reluctance on the part of plastic and reconstructive surgeons to precisely codify their sense of esthetics, no

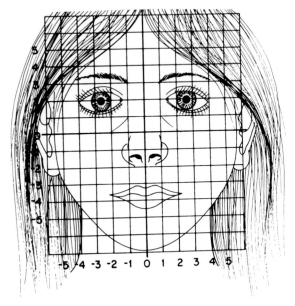

Figure 8. X-Y coordinate grid overlay used to precisely measure facial asymmetry.

doubt due to the belief that each case has its own unique set of esthetic considerations. To quote plastic surgeons Patterson and Powell ('74): "No standard norm can be slavishly followed; however, one can establish a fictional norm for each individual on the basis of the deformity encountered. Such a norm is desirable since criteria of ideal forms are by no means universally accepted."

MEASUREMENT FROM THE LATERAL ASPECT

The facial profile has received considerably more attention than the frontal aspect, both in terms of standardized measures and esthetic criteria. This is probably due, in part, to the relative ease of clinically altering anteroposterior discrepancies and the great difficulty in altering width dimensions.

As an introduction to profile measurements, some of the basic anatomical terminology used in this paper needs to be discussed. The *cranial base* is the bony structure on which the brain rests (Fig. 9). It is often considered to be a fixed plane in the skull, and distances and angles are measured with reference to the cranial base. The *maxilla* is simply the upper jaw, and the *mandible* is the lower jaw. Finally, *anterior* and *poste-*

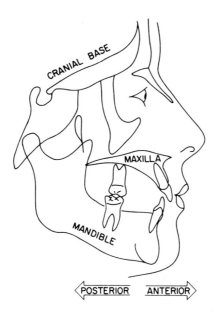

Figure 9. Basic anatomical structures used in craniofacial analysis.

rior are directions; anterior means toward the front of the face, and posterior means toward the back of the head.

Edward H. Angle, the father of orthodontics, made some of the first formal observations concerning profile esthetics and measurement in 1907. He considered the mouth to be the most important factor in determining esthetics of the face, and he believed that the beauty of the mouth depended on the dental occlusion or how well the teeth fit together. Angle developed a system for classifying the esthetic value of profiles based on the way the upper first molar and lower first molar are aligned. The Angle classification system produced three facial types. A dental Class I occlusion is one in which there is a normal molar relation (Fig. 10). It usually produces a profile in which the bridge of the nose, upper and lower lip, and chin fall on a straight vertical line. The other two facial types are considered abnormal, hence the molar relationship was labelled as a malocclusion. Dental Class II malocclusions are those in which the upper first molar lies in front of the lower first molar, relatively anterior to its normal position. This usually results in a retrognathic profile, with the chin and lower lip posterior to their normal position. Dental Class III malocclusions are those in which the position of the lower first molar is relatively anterior to its normal position, causing a prognathic profile, with the lower lip protruding in front of the upper lip.

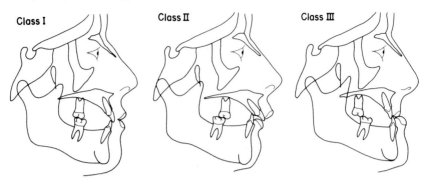

Figure 10. Angle's classification system of dental occlusion. Class I occlusions are normal occlusions. Class II malocclusions are those where the upper first molar lies in front of the lower first molar, usually resulting in the chin and lower lip posterior to their normal position. Class III malocclusions are those where the upper first molar lies behind the lower first molar, usually causing the lower lip to protrude in front of the upper lip.

Although Angle's classification system remains very popular today, it is still basically a dental classification system and tells very little about skeletal or soft tissue components of the facial profile. For example, in talking about a Class II molar relationship, one does not know whether the condition exists because of the relationship of the teeth, a long maxilla, a short mandible, or a combination of all three.

Other early orthodontists, such as Lischer ('26), Simon ('26) and Hellman ('39), advocated more comprehensive measurement and analysis of the facial profile. They constructed lines, angles, and proportions for diagnosis and classification either from photographs or directly on patients' faces. The development of cephalometrics through the use of X-rays by Broadbent and others in the 1930's provided the possibility of studying the underlying skeletal and dental structure along with the soft tissue profile.

In order to assure that there is comparability among photographs and X-rays of all individuals, standardized photographs and radiographs have typically been taken. These records are normally standardized in two ways. First, all photographs and X-rays are taken at a fixed distance from the target individual. The fixed distance from camera to target is necessary to insure size constancy among photographic and radiographic records. If two sets of records are taken at different fixed distances, they can be adjusted to the same scale by multiplying all corresponding distances by an enlargement or reduction factor. The second type of standardization is that of position: all targets are placed in fixed positions before being photographed or X-rayed. In order to maintain a standard head orientation, head holders are often used. These devices have rods that fit into the earholes and can be used to fix head rotation. Targets are also requested to close their mouths, bite down on their back teeth, and let their lips come together lightly. This additional procedure helps to standardize occlusion and facial expression.

Over the last fifty years, clinical researchers have developed a number of measures of the skull and its soft tissue drape. Many of the standard landmarks and measurements were derived from early anthropological studies which used the dry skull. Today, two types of cephalometric landmarks are generally used: those which are located on bone, cartilage or teeth are called hard tissue landmarks; those located on the external skin surface of the face are called soft tissue landmarks. Although as many as 300 landmarks can be used, most researchers use somewhere between 20 and 50 landmarks in their analyses.

There are three types of cephalometric landmarks: skeletal, dental, and soft tissue. Skeletal landmarks are used primarily to describe interrelationships among parts of the skeletal structure. For example, skeletal landmarks are used to determine how far forward the mandible is positioned relative to the maxilla or the cranial base. Dental landmarks, when used in conjunction with skeletal landmarks, are used to describe the relation of the teeth (primarily the upper and lower incisors) to each other and to selected skeletal structures. Soft tissue landmarks, when used in conjunction with skeletal landmarks, are used to measure the relative thickness of the musculature overlaying the skeleton.

Skeletal Landmarks

The vast majority of landmarks are skeletal. The following are a few representative profile landmarks which are used in the measures that will be subsequently discussed (Fig. 11). Points 1 through 3 describe the bony chin: *Menton* (1) is the most inferior point on the symphyseal outline. *Gnathion* (2) is the most anterior inferior point on the bony chin. *Pogonion* (3) is the most anterior point on the bony chin. *Point B* (4) is the most posterior point on the front surface of the chin between pogonion and infradentale. Points 6 and 15 describe the *lower incisor tip and root* respectively, while landmarks 7 and 12 describe the *upper incisor tip and root*. *Point A* (9) is the most posterior point on the curve of the maxilla. The *anterior nasal spine* (10) is the tip of the sharp bony process of the maxilla while the *posterior nasal spine* (45) is the most posterior point on the maxilla. *Gonion* (27) is the midpoint of the angle of the mandible. *Articulare* (31) is the intersection point of the inferior cranial base surface

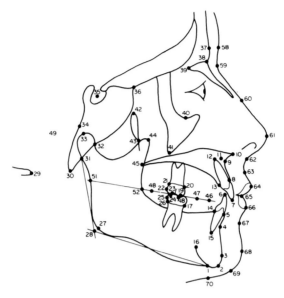

Figure 11. Cephalometric landmarks from the lateral aspect.

and the averaged posterior surface of the mandibular condyles. *Machine Porion* (49) is the midpoint of the line connecting the most superior point of the shadows of the ear rods of the cephalostat (*Anatomical Porion* is the most superior point of the external ear opening or external auditory meatus). *Sella turcica* (35) is the center of the pituitary fossa of the sphenoid bone. *Orbitale* (40) is the lowest point on the average of the right and left borders of the bony orbit. *Glabella* (37) is the most anterior point overlying the frontal sinus. Finally *Nasion* (38) is the most posterior point on the curvature at the bridge of the nose.

There is an additional series of soft tissue landmarks (Fig. 12), but many of them correspond to their hard tissue counterparts. *Soft glabella* (1) is the height of curvature of the soft tissue overlaying the frontal sinus. *Soft nasion* (2) is the most posterior superior point on the slope of the nose. *Nose tip* (4) is the most anterior point on the outline of the nose. *Soft subnasale* or *soft point A* (5) is the point at which the inferior slope of the nose merges with the upper lip. *Upper lip* or *labrale superius* (7) is the most anterior point of the upper lip. *Stomion* (8) is the intersection of the upper and lower lips. *Lower lip* or *labrale inferius* (9) is the most anterior point on the contour of the lower lip. *Soft point B* (10) is the point of greatest concavity where the lip joins the chin. *Soft pogonion* (11) is the most prominent or anterior part of the chin. *Soft gnathion* (12)

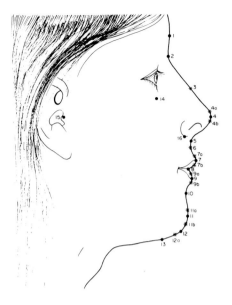

Figure 12. Soft tissue profile landmarks.

is the most anterior inferior point on the soft chin outline. *Soft menton* (13) is the point where the soft tissue seems to drop away from its close approximation to the bony chin. Finally, *tragion* (15), is the most anterior point in the supratragal notch of the ear.

The landmarks just described are used to make two basic kinds of measurements: linear and angular. Both types have advantages and disadvantages. Linear measurement is used to determine size, distance, and proportion. While proportions can be generalized from one target to another, size and distance comparisons are scale dependent. Targets must be converted to the same scale before using actual size and distance measurement. Angular measures are primarily used to describe relationships among planes in the face. They can be generalized across targets without size standardization, but it is impossible to determine the cause of differences in angular relations. Figure 13 illustrates this point using angle ABC, as defined by points A, B, and C. If angle ABC were to increase, we would be unable to tell whether the angle increased due to point A moving away from points B and C (Fig. 13-1) or point B moving down with respect to points A and C (Fig. 13-2) or finally point C moving up with respect to point A and point B (Fig. 13-3).

Those measures which provide the *best* general description of facial form have been selected for discussion here. Certain measures are favored over others primarily due to their heuristic value in describing

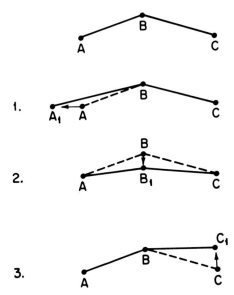

Figure 13. Three ways to increase angle ABC (after Moyers and Bookstein, '79).

regions of the face. Measures have been omitted which are very important to some individual clinicians in their diagnosis and treatment. However, specific capabilities of these measures to optimize soft tissue or dental esthetics or their stability over time limit their usefulness in general description.

Facial profile analysis usually combines the consideration of vertical and anteroposterior (horizontal) dimensions simultaneously because variation in one dimension is usually associated with variation in the other. However, for ease of presentation they will be considered separately, beginning with the vertical component.

Vertical Measurement of the Facial Profile

The primary purpose of vertical measurement is to determine whether the upper part of the face (between the brow ridge and the base of the nose) is generally in proportion with the lower part of the face (between the base of the nose and the chin). One way to conceptualize vertical relationships in the face is in terms of the interrelationship of horizontal planes. Six horizontal planes are commonly used in contemporary cephalometrics: the supraorbital plane, the sella-nasion plane, the Frankfort horizontal plane, the palatal plane, the functional occlusal plane, and the mandibular plane (Fig. 14).

Sassouni ('69) has illustrated how facial appearance changes when the

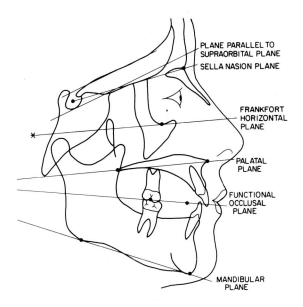

Figure 14. Horizontal facial planes.

interrelationship of these planes changes. For example, as the planes become more horizontal and nearly parallel, face height tends to approximate its breadth, and the face appears square from the frontal view. In this situation, the skull is often round with a bulging forehead, the bridge of the nose is usually low, and the nasal apertures are broad (Fig. 15). Lips tend to be thin, but lip height is excessive relative to face height. Finally, there is a prominent chin and a deep furrow between the lower lip and chin.

As the planes become more steep relative to each other, the face breadth tends to narrow, producing an ovoid appearance from the front (Fig. 16). The bridge of the nose is usually higher and the nasal apertures are narrow. Lips are usually broad but vertically short. The mouth is wide, and there is usually the lack of a chin.

The interrelationship of these planes can be more precisely determined by both angular and linear measurement. The most commonly used angular measurements are *sella-nasion to Frankfort plane*, *sella-nasion to palatal plane*, *sella-nasion to functional occlusal plane*, and *sella-nasion to mandibular plane* (Fig. 17). In the faces described above, where the planes are more horizontal and nearly parallel, the sella-nasion to palatal plane angle is approximately half the sella-nasion to mandibular plane angle. As the planes become more steep relative to each other, the sella-nasion to mandibular plane angle increases, with the sella-nasion to pala-

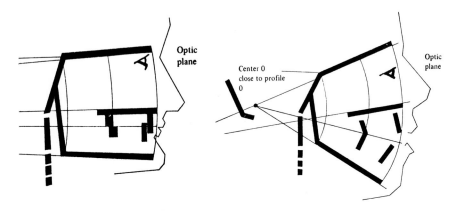

Figure 15. Square facial type with facial planes nearly parallel (from Sassouni, '59).

Figure 16. Ovoid facial type with facial planes more steep relative to each other (from Sassouni, '59).

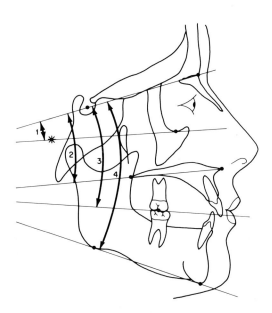

Figure 17. Angular skeletal measures of facial height. 1. Sella-nasion/Frankfort plane angle; 2. Sella-nasion/palatal plane angle; 3. Sella-nasion/functional occlusal plane angle; 4. Sella-nasion/mandibular plane angle.

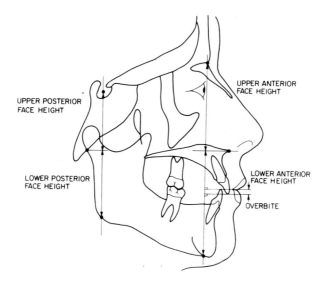

Figure 18. Linear, skeletal and dental measures of facial height.

tal plane angle shrinking to less than half the size of the sella-nasion to mandibular plane angle.

The most common linear measures of face height (Fig. 18) are *upper anterior face height*, the vertical distance from nasion to the palatal plane; *lower anterior face height*, the distance from the palatal plane to menton; *upper posterior face height*, the vertical distance from sella to a perpendicular from articulare; and *lower posterior face height*, the vertical distance from gonion to the perpendicular from articulare.

Many researchers use the ratio of these distances to describe vertical proportions of the face. To again use the faces described before (Figs. 15 and 16), when the planes in the face are more horizontal and nearly parallel, total posterior face height is nearly equal to total anterior face height, and lower anterior face height is smaller than upper anterior face height. As the planes become more steep relative to each other, total posterior face height lessens to nearly one-half the size of total anterior face height, and lower anterior face height tends to exceed upper anterior face height.

One additional linear measure of facial height, especially in the oral region, is overbite, a dental measure. It is defined as the vertical distance that the upper incisor overlaps the lower one. If there is no overlap, it is the vertical distance between incisor tips. As the degree of overbite increases, the lower face tends to foreshorten; as it decreases or tends toward an open bite, the lower face tends to lengthen.

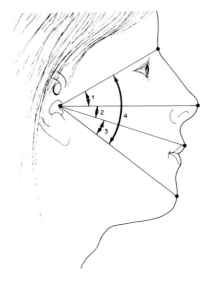

Figure 19. Angular soft tissue measures of facial height. 1. Nasal angle; 2. Maxillary angle; 3. Mandibular angle; 4. Total vertical angle.

Angular and linear vertical measurement of the face can also be performed using soft tissue landmarks from either photographic or radiographic representations. Peck and Peck ('70) have identified four angular measurements (Fig. 19) which can be used to measure vertical height: the *nasal angle*, defined by the intersection at tragion of lines from soft nasion and nose tip, measures nasal height; the *maxillary angle*, defined by the intersection at tragion of lines from nose tip and upper lip, measures maxillary height; the *mandibular angle*, defined by the intersection at tragion of lines from upper lip and soft pogonion, measures mandibular height; and finally, the total *vertical angle*, defined by the intersection at tragion of lines from soft nasion and soft pogonion, measures total face height.

In a similar manner, linear vertical measurement can be performed with soft tissue landmarks. For example, *upper anterior face height* can be represented as the vertical distance from soft nasion to the bottom of the nose (Fig. 20) and *lower anterior face height* can be measured as the vertical distance from the bottom of the nose to the bottom of the chin (soft menton).

The use of soft tissue landmarks allows for the measurement of some additional vertical dimensions. For example, *upper lip length* can be measured as the vertical distance from the bottom of the nose to the point of

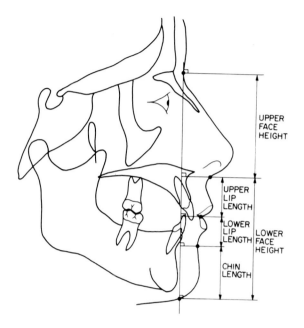

Figure 20. Linear soft tissue measures of facial height.

lip intersection. *Lower lip length* can be measured as the vertical distance from the point of lip intersection to soft point B, the point of greatest concavity below the lower lip. *Chin length* can be measured as the vertical distance from soft point B to soft menton, the bottom of the chin.

Anteroposterior Facial Measurement

While the esthetics of vertical facial proportion have received considerable interest, anteroposterior positioning of facial structures has received the lion's share of research. Anteroposterior measures, like vertical measures, are of two types: angular and linear; and skeletal, dental, and soft tissue landmarks are used.

Skeletal measures of anteroposterior variability have concentrated on the relative position of three structures: the cranial base, the maxilla and the mandible. Three of the most common angular measures of anteroposterior variability are *sella to nasion to A point* (SNA), *sella to nasion to B point* (SNB), and *A point to nasion to B point* (ANB) (Fig. 21). The cranial base, as measured by sella-nasion, is often considered to be a fixed plane, and so the angle SNA describes the degree to which the maxilla is positioned anteriorly with reference to sella-nasion. Likewise,

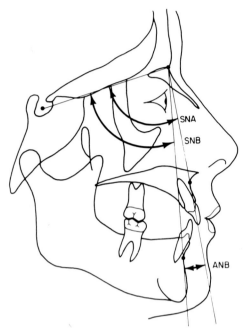

Figure 21. Three angular measures of anteroposterior variability. SNA measures the degree to which the maxilla is positioned anteriorly with reference to sella-nasion. SNB represents the degree to which the mandible is positioned anteriorly with reference to sella nasion. ANB measures the amount of discrepancy in anterior positioning of mandible and maxilla.

the angle SNB represents the degree to which the mandible is positioned anteriorly with reference to sella-nasion. Angle ANB is used to measure the amount of discrepancy in anterior positioning of the mandible and maxilla.

Several linear measurements of skeletal structure have also been used. These include *anterior cranial base length*, *maxillary length* and *mandibular length* (Fig. 22) and their effective lengths (their projected lengths on a horizontal plane; Fig. 23). These measurements are used to describe face depth, as well as balance between the lengths of the maxilla and mandible.

Dental measures of anteroposterior variability have dealt primarily with the relation of the upper and lower incisors to the skeletal structure and to each other. In terms of angular measurement, the *upper incisor to sella-nasion* angle describes the degree to which the upper incisor is angled anteriorly, or sticks out; the *lower incisor to mandibular plane angle*

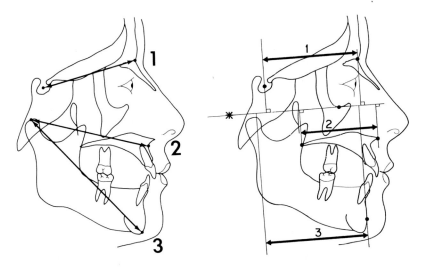

Figure 22. Linear measures of (1) sella-nasion, (2) maxillary length and (3) mandibular length.

Figure 23. Linear measures of the effective lengths of (1) sella-nasion, (2) maxillary length, and (3) mandibular length.

describes the degree to which the lower incisor is angled anteriorly, and the *upper incisor to lower incisor angle* describes the relative angle of the incisors (Fig. 24). The primary linear measurement, which describes the horizontal relationship of the upper and lower incisors, is termed *overjet*. The more anterior the upper incisor relative to the lower incisor, the more overjet.

Soft tissue measures of anteroposterior variability comprise the largest category of anteroposterior measurements. They fall into two groups: those which describe the Gestalt of the profile and are not sensitive to specific facial structures, and those which concentrate on anteroposterior variability of specific structures. The primary angular measure of the facial "Gestalt" is the *soft facial convexity angle* (Fig. 25). It is the angle formed by the soft glabella, nose tip, and soft pogonion; and it describes the "pointedness" of the facial profile. Faces become more convex or pointed as the nose lengthens, the chin retrudes, or as a combination of the two occurs.

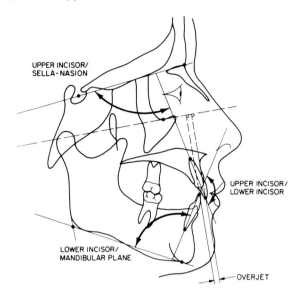

Figure 24. Dental measures of anteroposterior variability.

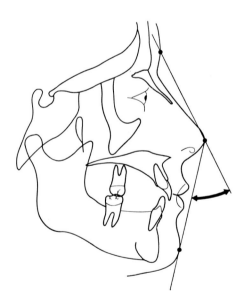

Figure 25. Soft facial convexity angle.

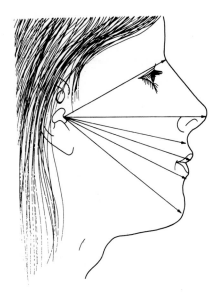

Figure 26. Soft tissue facial depth.

Soft tissue facial depth is determined via linear measurement (Fig. 26). Tragion is used as the base point, and the distances to soft nasion, nose tip, soft point A, upper lip, lower lip and soft pogonion are all used as measures of facial depth.

Clinicians have devoted most of their time developing measurement techniques for the lower third of the face. There has been particular interest in describing the interrelationship of the upper lip, the lower lip, and the chin. Three soft tissue angular measures have been commonly used in general description of the lower third of the face. The *soft profile angle*, as defined by soft glabella, soft point A and soft pogonion, is normally used to indicate the degree to which pogonion and the soft tissue overlay deviate from the plane of soft glabella to soft point A (Fig. 27). The *maxillofacial angle* is defined by soft pogonion, soft nasion and upper lip (Fig. 28). It measures the degree to which the upper lip protrudes from the soft nasion to soft pogonion plane. Finally, the *Holdaway angle*, defined by the intersection of lines from nasion to point B and from upper lip to soft pogonion, measures the degree to which the upper lip and soft tissue chin deviate from the skeletal plane nasion to point B.

There are innumerable soft tissue linear measurements of anteroposte-

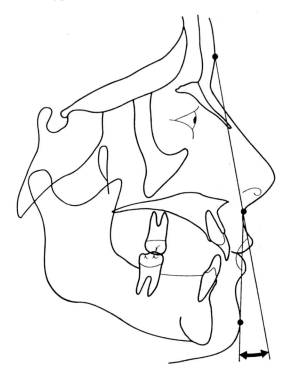

Figure 27. Soft profile angle.

rior variability of the lips and chin. Some are measured from the surface of the teeth to the most anterior soft tissue point, while others are measured from the skull to the soft tissue points. For the purpose of this paper, the method of measuring soft tissue thickness which is the simplest and easiest to present has been selected (Fig. 29). It is performed by locating the hard and soft tissue landmarks, constructing a Frankfort horizontal plane, dropping perpendiculars from the landmarks to the plane, and measuring horizontal distances between hard and soft tissue landmarks. For example, what has been illustrated here is the soft tissue thickness at soft point A, the upper lip, the lower lip, soft point B, and pogonion or soft chin button.

The nasal region has received considerably less research interest than has the lower face. Nonetheless, angular and linear measures have been developed to characterize the nose. There are two soft tissue angular measurements most commonly used in plastic and orthognathic surgery (Fig. 30). The *nasofacial angle* is formed by the intersection of the line from soft glabella to soft pogonion with the plane of the bridge of the nose, defining protrusion of the nose from the facial plan. The *columel-*

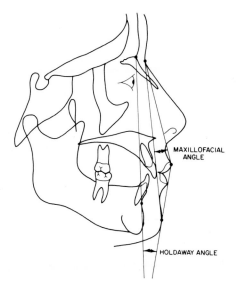

Figure 28. Maxillofacial and Holdaway angles.

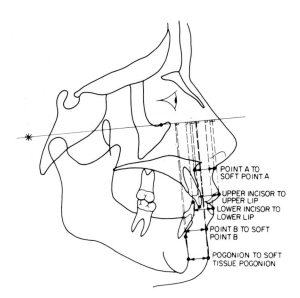

Figure 29. Soft tissue thickness.

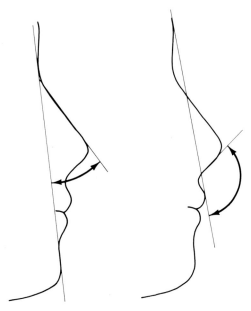

Figure 30. Nasofacial and columellar-to-lip angles (after Broadbent and Matthews, '57).

lar to lip angle (naso-labial angle) is formed by the intersection of the line from upper lip to glabella and the lower border of the nose, describing the vertical angulation of the nose tip.

Linear measurements of nose length use the distance from hard tissue landmarks to soft tissue landmarks as projected on the Frankfort horizontal plane (Fig. 31). *Upper nose length* is the horizontal distance from nasion to the tip of the nose. *Nose depth* is the horizontal distance from the anterior nasal spine to the nose tip, and *lower nose length* is the horizontal distance from soft point A to the tip of the nose.

RESEARCH ON FACIAL ESTHETICS

The cephalometric measures described above, along with others not described here, have been used in clinical studies of esthetic preferences for over thirty years. There have been two general approaches to the study of facial esthetics. One approach tries to identify subjects who are considered to be physically attractive and to determine what physical attributes make them attractive. These subjects are usually public figures celebrated for their good looks, but occasionally they are just individuals judged to have good facial esthetics by a group of clinical practitioners. These individuals are photographed and X-rayed in standard positions,

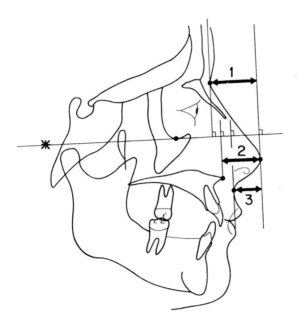

Figure 31. Linear measures of (1) upper nose length, (2) anterior nasal spine-to-nose tip and (3) lower nose length.

and cephalometric measures are obtained from these records. Their average values on selected anthropometric measures often serve as norms representing the public's esthetic taste. Peck and Peck's ('70) research is representative of this first type of study. They chose to assess the public's facial esthetic preferences by selecting beauty contest winners, professional models, and actors and actresses for their sample. Each of the 49 females and 3 males were photographed in standard position, and lateral cephalograms were taken. It was discovered that all targets had normal Class I molar relationships. When sample means were compared to those taken from orthodontic samples, it was also found that the public preferred a fuller, more protrusive dentofacial pattern than has been set as customary cephalometric standards.

The other approach commonly used in the study of facial esthetics requires one group of individuals to evaluate the attractiveness of another group of individuals. The individuals evaluated are usually chosen either to represent a normal population or to represent variability on particular dimensions. Faces are presented either from the frontal or lateral perspective, and they are depicted with either line drawings, silhouettes, or facial photographs. Normally, the subjects have been evaluated using cephalometric measurement techniques, and variability in these anthropometric

73

measures is correlated with variability in attractiveness judgments to determine which physical dimensions are related to esthetic judgments.

The work of Cox and van der Linden ('71) illustrates this second type of study. The authors randomly selected a group of 87 male and 87 female targets from over 400 dental school records. These records included people with good and poor facial esthetics. Silhouette outlines of the targets were then given to a group of individuals, who were asked to discriminate between the most and least attractive profiles using a Q-sort technique. Eighteen males and 18 females with the best rated facial harmony and 18 males and 18 females with the poorest rated facial harmony were identified. The group with good facial esthetics was compared to that with poor facial esthetics on selected hard and soft tissue measures. Cox and van der Linden reported that targets judged to have poor facial esthetics generally had more convex faces and greater soft tissue thickness in the lower third of the face. Larger convexity was primarily due to anterior positioning of the skeletal, dental, and soft tissue structures in the midface.

Research using frontal representations of the face has been much rarer than that using profile representations. To date, only two studies have attempted to relate esthetic judgment to frontal measurement. Both studies have discussed attractiveness, or cuteness, in infants. Sternglanz and co-workers ('77) simulated infant faces; Hildebrant and Fitzgerald ('79) used frontal photographs. They both found that infants with short and narrow features, large eyes and pupils, and larger foreheads were rated as "cuter."

While considerable research on facial esthetics has attempted to define norms for what is attractive or preferred in this society, very little work has sought to determine the range of what is acceptable, and conversely, unacceptable. While attractiveness norms are very important in clinical work, as they provide general treatment goals for the practitioner, knowledge of the range of acceptable appearance is equally important because of the potentially devastating social consequences of having an unacceptable appearance. Unattractive individuals, solely as a result of their appearances, are likely to receive relatively consistent negative social reactions from others. This treatment ultimately can result in the internalization of lower aspirations and self image, and even different personality styles (Adams, '78).

Defining the range of acceptable appearance is a very difficult task which needs to be approached in several steps. Research should first be performed at the gross, macroscopic level to clearly identify regions of the face that are consistently correlated with esthetic judgments. These studies should maximize generality by using as many facial types and age groups as possible. Once physical dimensions have been identified, the next step is to focus on each dimension and to establish, in a controlled experimental setting, an acceptability range.

For the last several years Dr. Lee Graber and I have been working on a project exploring interrelationships between an individual's own facial form, his self-image, and his evaluation of others. The general research procedure has been to have subjects evaluate a series of slides representing selected dimensions such as normality/abnormality of appearance, physical attractiveness, or personality, after which they are requested to fill out a battery of questionnaires measuring self-concept, body image and dentofacial awareness. Finally, on a subsequent day, they are given a complete orthodontic examination and are photographed in the standard position.

The study that is pertinent to the topic of this paper is one in which we attempted to identify facial dimensions which are related to positive and negative esthetic judgments made by children. A group of boys and girls ranging in age from 10 to 13 years were asked to make esthetic judgments about a group of 58 same-aged children who were presented via a series of slides which simultaneously revealed both a side profile and frontal view. Subjects were asked to identify those target children who had something wrong with their eyes, nose, mouth, jaws, chin, or shape of face. The instructions were purposely vague so as not to cue the children to attend to particular facial features.

The target sample fell within the normal range of facial appearance. None had obvious stigmata (e.g., birthmarks, cleft lip, scarring, or major structural deformation). Thirty male and 28 female children were chosen for the study from a population of over 600 taken from the files of a university dental school. It was decided to use dental school records because cephalograms were necessary for later anatomical analyses, and it was not ethically possible to X-ray a random sample of children. Each record contained standarized full frontal and lateral cephalograms as well as frontal and lateral photographs.

In order to insure that targets did not over-represent visible problems associated with the oral region, the sample was chosen using Sassouni's ('69) facial form classification system. This system divides the population into nine groups based on a combination of anteroposterior and vertical dimensions and allows a general categorization of facial type. A final selection of targets was based on both representativeness of facial type as well as varied level of attractiveness within each facial type. Post hoc cephalometric comparisons of the target sample with two normative samples (those of Riolo et al. ('74) and Ackerman and Proffit ('74) revealed no significant differences in either means or standard deviations between the sample and the normative population on over 100 cephalometric measures.

As a preliminary to the actual analysis, frontal and lateral radiographs of each of the 58 targets were traced and computerized. One hundred and four distance measures, 23 proportion measures (ratios of distance), and 45 angular measures were derived from the radiographs. These measurements included all those discussed before as well as frontal, soft tissue measures such as intraocular distance, eye length and width, eyebrow length, nose length and width, mouth length and width, and facial width and length. The percentage of "nothing wrong" judgments were next computed for each of the targets, with boys and girls analyzed separately.

Next, rank-order correlations were computed—separately by target sex and subject sex—relating the cephalometric measures to subjects' "nothing wrong" judgments.

Since correlations were calculated using over 150 cephalometric measures, it was decided to use the .01 significance level as the criterion. Nonetheless, 19 cephalometric variables were found to be significantly related to the dependent variable for male targets, and 37 were significantly related for female targets. Correlations were remarkably similar across subject sex: there was overlap in the judgments on 14 of the 17 variables for male targets and 33 of the 37 variables for female targets. It was therefore decided to collapse across subject sex and recompute correlation coefficients.

Table 1 presents a selected sample of the cephalometric variables which were significantly related to "nothing wrong" judgments. As stated before, many of these variables were highly correlated so that another variable could have been substituted for several of these, but this group has been chosen for its explanatory power.

All variables listed in the first column, except one, related to anteroposterior variability. Facial width was the only measurement from the frontal aspect found to be significantly correlated with "nothing wrong" judgments, and that was only the case for female targets. There were over 60 variables measured from the frontal aspect—both from hard and soft tissue landmarks, including measures of the eyes, nose, and mouth—and none of these other variables were related to evaluations in the sample.

In looking at the correlation coefficients for male and female targets, the only variable which was significantly related to "nothing wrong" judgments for both male and female targets was the Holdaway angle (Fig. 28), which measures the straightness of the facial profile (excluding the nose). The negative sign of the correlation indicates that more "nothing wrong" judgments were made about straighter profiles.

Except for the Holdaway angle, the pattern of correlations was very different for male and female targets. The variables correlated with "nothing wrong" judgments for male targets appear to be related to the lower

Table 1. Selected cephalometric variables significantly related to "nothing wrong" judgments

	Correlation for Male Targets (N = 30)	Correlation for Female Targets (N = 28)
Soft Tissue Variables		
Holdaway Angle	−.51*	−.58*
Distance From Upper Incisor to Upper Lip	.04	.54*
Distance From Point B To Soft Point B	−.48*	−.18
Distance From Pogonion To Soft Pogonion	−.57*	.03
Facial Width (Distance)	−.35	.52*
Dental Variables		
Upper Incisor to Sella-Nasion Plane (Angle)	.17	−.59*
Lower Incisor to Mandibular Plane (Angle)	−.57*	.15
Overjet (Distance)	−.45	−.58*
Skeletal Variables		
SNA (Angle)	.18*	−.05
SNB (Angle)	.52*	−.06
ANB (Angle)	−.54*	−.15

*$p < .01$

jaw. Note that the distance from point B to soft point B and pogonion to soft pogonion are tissue thickness measures over the lower jaw. The lower incisor to mandibular plane angle describes the angle of the lower front teeth relative to the lower jaw, and SNB and ANB describe the relationship of the lower jaw to the cranial base and upper jaw. For females, the variables correlated with "nothing wrong" judgments seem to be related to the upper jaw structures. For example, distance from upper incisor to upper lip describes the thickness of the upper lip; upper incisor to sella-nasion angle describes the angle of the upper front teeth relative to the upper jaw; and overjet describes the degree that the upper teeth overlap the lower ones. Since the Holdaway angle was the best single predictor for both sexes, it was decided to explore the make-up of the Holdaway angle in terms of other measures to get some notion as to what might be "driving" it in this sample. The correlations (Table 2) again indicated that the Holdaway angle was most highly correlated with lower jaw variables for male targets and upper jaw variables for female targets.

Table 2. Correlations of Holdaway angle with constituent soft tissue, dental and skeletal measures

	Correlation for Male Targets (N = 30)	Correlation for Female Targets (N = 28)
Soft Tissue Measures		
Distance From Upper		
Incisor to Upper Lip	−.22	−.49*
Distance From Pogonion		
To Soft Tissue Pogonion	.20	−.18
Dental Measures		
Upper Incisor To		
Sella-Nasion Plane (Angle)	−.04	.27
Lower Incisor To		
Mandibular Plane (Angle)	.56*	.42
Overjet (Distance)	.19	.61*
Skeletal Measures		
SNA	−.03	.65*
SNB	−.56*	.14

*$p < .01$

What conclusions can be drawn from these data? First, and most importantly, this study has established that evaluative judgments of facial appearance can be related to groups of facial features using life-like representations of real people and not line drawings or silhouettes. With regard to the dimensions identified, I would not contend that these are the primary dimensions on which evaluative judgments of the face are made, but they make good candidates for the list. The size of the target sample needs to be greatly increased before we can confidently speak about important dimensions of facial appearance.

In finding no differences in the way males and females evaluate target subjects, the results support the contention that our society has a clear standard for facial appearance. The correlations also indicate that judgments of both male and female targets might be tapping the same underlying dimension, which could be "straightness of facial profile."

These data are quite remarkable because the overwhelming majority of measures found to be related to esthetic judgments were measures of anteroposterior variability. This finding is especially novel for someone, such as myself, coming from a tradition which does not typically consider facial profile. In this regard, I believe that traditional physical attractiveness research has introduced some serious artifacts because of its reliance on frontal photographs. Normally, people are seen in three dimensions and therefore from more than one perspective, including a lateral one. The current approach moves one step closer to an accurate pictorial representation of the target population.

The intent of this paper was to give a psychologists' perspective on research in facial esthetics. The work that has been done in the separate fields of psychology and dentistry was reviewed, and an attempt made to outline some of the vast area which remains to be explored. As a final comment, I would like to make a "pitch" for more interdisciplinary research. My work with orthodontists and plastic surgeons over the last several years has brought me a much broader perspective with which to tackle new research issues. It is my belief that it is only through these multiple perspectives that we can hope to understand the complex problems in human behavior which we have chosen to address.

REFERENCES

Angle, E. H. *Malocclusion of the Teeth*. S. S. White Co., 1907.

Broadbent, T. R. and V. L. Matthews. Artistic relationships in surface anatomy of the face: application to reconstructive surgery. Plast. Reconstr. Surg. 20:1-12, 1957.

Cox, N. H. and F. van der Linden. Facial harmony. Am. J. Orthodont. 60(2):175-183, 1971.

Hellman, M. Some facial features and their orthodontic implications. Am. J. Orthodont. 25:922-951, 1939.

Hildebrant, K. A. and H. E. Fitzgerald. Facial feature determinants of perceived infant attractiveness. Infant Behav. Develop. 2:329-339, 1979.

Krogman, W. M. and V. Sassouni. *A Syllabus of Roentgenographic Cephalometry*. University Microfilm, Ann Arbor, 1957.

Lischer, B. Photography for orthodontists. Int. J. Orthodont. 19:27-35, 1926.

Moyers, R.E. and F. Bookstein. The inappropriateness of convential cephalometrics. Am. J. Orthodont. 75:599-617, 1979.

Patterson, C. N. and D. G. Powell. Facial analysis in patient evaluation for physiologic and cosmetic surgery. Laryngoscope 84(6):1004-1019, 1979.

Peck, H. and S. Peck. A concept of facial esthetics. Angle Orthodont. 40:284-318, 1970.

Sassouni, V. *The Face in Five Dimensions*. Philadelphia Center for Research in Child Growth, University of Pennsylvania.

Sassouni, V. A classification of skeletal facial types. Am. J. Orthodont. 55(2):104-123, 1969.

Simon, P. *Fundamental Principles of Systematic Diagnosis of Dental Anomalies*. The Stratford Co., Boston, 1926.

Sternglanz, S., J. L. Gray and M. Murakami. Adult preferences in infantile facial features: an ethological approach. Animal Behav. 25:108-115, 1977.

PSYCHOLOGICAL CONSIDERATIONS OF ORTHODONTIC TREATMENT

Lee W. Graber, D.D.S., Ph.D.

Associate Professor, Loyola University
Research Scientist, Division of Oral Biology,
American Dental Association

At first glance, the disciplines of social psychology and clinical orthodontics would seem to be as separate as any two disciplines one could find. As Miller and Larson ('79) have stated, "One is mental, the other is dental." Indeed, it is difficult to bring these two sciences together. One involves clinical treatment; the other is a social science. The clinician measures physical characteristics with direct precision in terms of millimeters and degrees; the psychologist measures less specific entities, such as verbal and social actions and attitudes. Yet while these two sciences appear to be dichotomous, there are areas of overlap where interdisciplinary considerations are both useful and necessary.

This paper discusses several areas of commonality where the field of psychology has allowed the orthodontist to better understand the motivating factors behind—and the behavior patterns of—individuals who seek orthodontic corrective care. Consideration will be made of the social-psychological background that leads an individual to seek correction in dentofacial form. Additionally, behavioral characteristics of patients that contribute to the success of treatment will be discussed. The interaction between objective evaluations of anatomical facial characteristics and self-satisfaction will also be explored, along with a discussion of the role of facial form balance and esthetics in self-esteem. Finally, the sociopsychological changes resulting from alterations of facial form due to orthodontic plus facial surgery treatment will be considered.

Current statistics provided by the American Association of Orthodontists indicate that the average orthodontic practice case load is composed of a wide range of orthodontic problems, with patients ranging in age from newborn infants to senior citizens. The past fifteen years has seen a change in the make-up of orthodontic practices, from those solely characterized by teenage patients to those now including (1) a large number of younger children under early orthodontic guidance, (2) adult orthodontic patients, and (3) a large pre-teen, as well as teenage, group. It is generally agreed that most patients seek orthodontic care for dentofacial es-

81

thetic purposes (Walley, '52; Secord and Backman, '59; Lewit and Virolainen, '68; Cohen, '70; Stricker, '70; Stricker *et al.*, '79), Parents usually initiate orthodontic consultation for children, while an adult must be self-motivated to seek professional care.

THE CHILD PATIENT

The topic of motivation for orthodontic treatment for the child can be best understood using three questions. First, what are the pressures that influence parents to have their children undergo corrective care? Second, what are the social and attitudinal differences between those youngsters needing care who actually seek treatment and those youngsters who need therapy but do not desire it? Third, what is the sociopsychological profile of the "motivated" child?

Parental Motivation

The classical research study of parental motivations for seeking care for their children was completed by Baldwin and colleagues (Baldwin and Barnes, '65, '66; Baldwin *et al.*, '67). Over 375 patients and parents were surveyed by means of a detailed questionnaire. A variety of sociopsychological factors were evaluated, including: socioeconomic background, ethnic identity, motivation, dental health, previous experience with orthodontic care, and personality characteristics of the child. Results indicated that the mother was usually the primary motivating individual in the family and that many of these mothers had orthodontic problems that were treated when they were children. Some mothers seemed to feel guilty about passing on "inherited" traits to their children, and this guilt impelled them to seek treatment for their children. Fathers exhibited only casual interest in treatment, with the exception of some who were interested in providing care for their daughters.

More detailed analysis of an additional 250 cases (Baldwin *et al.*, '67) suggests that parents often have very complex motivational drives. In some cases, the parents may attempt to resolve problems of their own self-esteem through identification with their child and the child's therapy. Parents, particularly those who resemble their children and who did not have the benefit of care, may be especially sensitized by their child's problem and will "not want their child to go through what they went through." Requests for treatment by these parents may be either for conspicuous orthodontic problems or for more minor problems that are conceived by the parents to be abnormalities in dentofacial form.

A less common motivation by some parents is an attempt to resolve "insoluble" family health problems by displacing them onto their child's orthodontic problem and its treatment. There may be an overly energetic focus of attention on the dentofacial problem with hopes that—through its treatment—the other health problems will disappear. This schema is sometimes extended to the situation where there is another family member with a more difficult health or social problem—but because the prospective orthodontic patient has a more easily identifiable and rectifiable problem, his care is given priority.

The final motivating consideration revolves around the achievement orientation of parents. The parent who brings his child in for treatment is often an upwardly striving and aspiring individual who sees orthodontic treatment as a badge of social belonging or acceptance. Parents often make the decision for treatment based on their own social aspirations, cultural values and attitudes, believing that treatment will lead to improved social and work possibilities for their children in later life. The predominance of young girls in orthodontic practices is explained by the sex differential in social ideals for "attractive" dentofacial characteristics (Walley, '52; Lewit and Virolainen, '68; Lerner et al., '76). There are more social rewards for attractiveness for females, and hence it is more important for females to have good facial esthetics than it is for males. Parents recognize this attractiveness value differential, seeing straight and even teeth and a pretty smile as more important attributes for girls, even if their own child undergoing orthodontic treatment is a boy (Baldwin et al., '67).

One may conclude from these studies that while impaired function of the teeth is a factor for some parents in seeking care for their children, most parents focus on social and psychological handicaps due to perceived or actual facial disproportions (Secord and Backman, '59; Howitt et al., '67; Hilzenrath and Baldwin, '71). Parents see the benefits of dental and facial form alteration in terms of personal and social gain rather than biologic or physiologic improvement.

Seeker Versus Non-Seeker

Warford ('73) compared the differences in motivation for orthodontic treatment between youngsters who had sought orthodontic care and those who had not sought treatment. Fifty-eight (32 girls and 26 boys) seventh and eighth grade prospective patients from the Northwestern University Dental Clinic were given a forty-item questionnaire. An analogous group of fifty teenagers (31 girls and 19 boys) were given the same questionnaire at a local junior high school, along with an orthodontic evaluation. The scores from the orthodontic evaluation (Occlusal Index, Summers, '71) revealed that 91.4% of the clinic sample and 64.0% of the school sample were in need of corrective orthodontic treatment. Statistical analyses indicated that the youngsters actively seeking care were less satisfied with their teeth and attached more value to straight teeth than did the children in the school sample. Additionally, the patient group expected orthodontic treatment to fulfill certain sociopsychological needs, including increased popularity, improved speech, better looks, less teasing about appearance, and more friends. The clinic sample did not consider pain, teasing or change of their appearance during treatment as important in their decision to have appliances. Those youngsters not seeking care were less likely to see orthodontic treatment as providing either social or dental-functional results, i.e., they had less faith that orthodontics would be beneficial to them in any way. Interestingly, these comparisons held up even when the sample was divided by sex.

As in the studies cited above, Warford ('73) found that parental influence and not degree of malocclusion was the key factor in whether or not the child sought corrective care. In the clinic sample, *both* parents usually deemed orthodontic care to be important to their child, while parents of the school children who needed treatment did not feel orthodontic care was necessary. The child's attitude toward prospective care was reflective of the opinions held by his parents.

Rosenberg ('75) has suggested that the parent and the dentofacially abnormal child set up self-concept defenses if the parent decides not to seek corrective treatment. One cannot deny that a dental or facial disproportion is unesthetic, as this would require a break with social reality. On the other hand, the parent can indicate to the child that the defect in appearance "really does not matter" and that there are other qualities that are much more important. This selective attribution of values by the parent is most likely to be adopted as a social defense by the child. Even if the parent is unable to rearrange his social values and adequately conceal his real feelings from the child, the child will be motivated to go along with the deception. Finally, Rosenberg notes that the child will selectively attribute to the parents an interest in those personality factors in which he is strong and lack of concern in deficient characteristics. This coping method certainly helps in supporting the child's self-regard.

The Motivated Child

While the above studies document the importance of parental influence on the child's motivation toward therapy, as well as coping mechanisms used by those who elect not to have needed treatment, it was studies by Virolainen and Lewit (Virolainen, '67; Lewit and Virolainen, '68) that accurately catalogued personality characteristics of those youngsters actually desiring orthodontic care. The subjects of this study were 129 Caucasian eighth grade students selected from a larger group on the basis of the

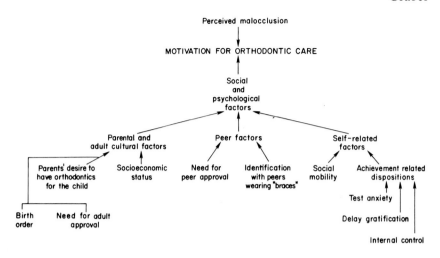

Figure 1. Social and psychological factors which influence patient motivation for orthodontic treatment. Model is redrawn after Virolainen, 1967, with permission.

presence of a malocclusion. The Eastman Esthetic Index (Howitt *et al.*, '67) and a general orthodontic rating (good occlusion, minor, moderate, major, severe malocclusion) were used to divide the group into those with a moderate malocclusion (N=95), good occlusion (N=24) and those with severe malocclusion (N=10). Virolainen postulated that there were a number of social and psychological factors, as well as the perception of the malocclusion, that influenced the prospective orthodontic patient (Fig. 1). To test this model, a series of questionnaires was developed and administered to the children.

The first major area tested was the importance of parental values and other adult cultural factors. Several factors influence a child's dependence on his parents' views. For example, it has been demonstrated that first-born children are more likely to internalize their parents' values and desire more parental approval than younger brothers and sisters. Therefore, it was suggested that first-born children will have a higher desire for treatment than younger siblings if they believe their parents favor orthodontic care. Need for adult approval is more important for some youngsters. Those who have a high need for adult approval are more likely to want to do what their parents suggest. To test need for adult approval, a subset of questions from the Children's Social Desirability Scale (Crandall *et al.*, '65) were included in the test questions.

Socioeconomic status has also been postulated to be a motivating factor for therapy (Baldwin and Barnes, '65, '66; Linn, '66; MacGregor, '67, '70; Cohen, '70; Stricker, '70). Middle and upper socioeconomic status individuals see good dental health and an attractive smile as valued characteristics and, therefore, are more likely to seek the services of a dental specialist than lower social class individuals, except in an emergency situation. Lower socioeconomic class individuals do not see dental care in terms of long-range health, but instead view it as an immediate solution for the problem of discomfort. Surveys seem to support the view that middle and upper social class families are predominant in orthodontic practices (Walley, '52; Warford, '73). To test the importance of socioeconomic factors, a segment of the questionnaire was devoted to surveying parental educational level, job classification, supervisory status, occupational attire, etc., in a manner that allowed development of a "prestige and educational score" (Reiss, '62).

The second major area tested in Virolainen's model was the importance of peer group factors. It has been well documented that, as the child continues through adolescence, he becomes less reliant on parental opinions and control and more responsive to peer group pressures and self-generated ideas (Erikson, '68; Jersild, '68; McCandless, '70). Do children who have a high need for peer approval react negatively to wearing unsightly orthodontic appliances that might cause ridicule or teasing? The long-term benefits of therapy might well be outweighed by the immediate concerns of looking different from their friends. A special series of questions was designed to measure both need for peer approval and the need for identification with other youngsters who might be wearing orthodontic appliances.

The third and final area tested concerned components of self-concept, including social aspirations and achievement motivation. For girls, in particular, physical attractiveness is seen as a means of social advancement, specifically in obtaining a suitable marriage partner, although boys may also view their general physical attractiveness as being important in obtaining jobs that require personal influence (see papers by Berschied and Adams in this volume). Since improved physical appearance is an outcome of orthodontic care, it was expected that those individuals with strong social aspirations might also desire orthodontic care to improve their future lot. The Epps-Montague scale of attitudes toward social mobility was chosen to assess this factor (Montague and Epps, '58).

Need for social achievement was also evaluated through the use of Bialer's Locus of Control Scale (Bialer, '61). This test measures the individual's view of himself as either (1) important in controlling his world (strong internal control) or (2) submissive to chance and the will of parents and peers (strong external control). Those individuals who have strong internal control and strong achievement motivation were predicted to react more favorably to orthodontic care. It was also presumed that those individuals who could look toward their future adult social goals would more readily accept the inconveniences of wearing unsightly appliances in their teen years (Warford, '73). Questions were added to assess this delayed gratification ability factor in patient motivation (Mischel, '62). Finally, Sarason's Test Anxiety Questionnaire (Sarason *et al.*, '60) was included as an additional measure of achievement motivation.

Results of this multifactored questionnaire supported the findings of Baldwin and Barnes ('66, '67) and Warford ('73) in that prospective patient desires for orthodontic care had the highest correlation with perceived parental wishes.

Birth order was not a significant factor, suggesting that orthodontic problems are not important enough to the parents to differentially affect the first-born child's constellation of needs.

Interestingly, general need for adult approval (social desirability) was a strong factor with many youngsters indicating greater desire for orthodontic care, *regardless* of whether or not their parents wanted them to receive care. This probably reflects a need for approval from significant other adults in the child's environment, i.e., his teachers, television role models, etc., whom the child perceives to value the results of orthodontic care.

Socioeconomic status of the child was also an important motivational control, especially for girls. Those girls at the higher socioeconomic levels and those at the lower socioeconomic levels valued dental care and its physical/social benefits more than those at the middle levels. The desire for orthodontic care seen in individuals from the lower socioeconomic level was based on the hope that its esthetic benefits would help to raise these individuals to a higher social level. These hopes were present even with the knowledge that orthodontic care might not be available to them.

Need for peer approval was not found to be a detrimental factor in adolescents' desire for orthodontics. Additionally, answers from this segment indicated that adolescents in general are not wholly negative in their attitudes toward wearing appliances. This may be due in part to the increased number of youngsters wearing the appliances and their value as a badge of higher socioeconomic status (Baldwin and Barnes, '67). As an ancillary finding, it was noted that youngsters with severe malocclusions were more negative in their evaluation of "kids with braces" than those with mild malocclusion or normal occlusion. Perception of malocclusion will be discussed later in this paper.

Social mobility or striving for a higher social status did not correlate with motivation for therapy except for those youngsters whose parents wanted them to undergo treatment. Parents who want their children to undergo treatment, and who see treatment as a cosmetic service, probably have underlying social motivations of their own, as previously discussed. It is not unreasonable to assume that some of the parental motivations, e.g., improved social class and improved job opportunities, were delineated for the child at the time the subject of orthodontics was discussed.

The tests for internal versus external control and delayed gratification abilities had very low positive correlations with desire for treatment. The results suggest that these teenagers saw the decision to go to an orthodontist as out of their hands and unrelated to their personal achievement undertakings. This finding underscores the importance of parental input into the child's decision to have orthodontic treatment.

The final section of the questionnaire, which evaluated test anxiety, indicated a positive correlation between test anxiety and desire for orthodontic care. Further analysis revealed that test anxiety was strongly linked with dependency on parental views, particularly in the high socioeconomic group. Those subjects that scored as test-anxious, or who showed high need for adult approval, tended to conform to their parents' wishes. Those subjects who were neither test-anxious nor in need of adult approval made decisions relative to orthodontic care independent of their parents' desires.

In sum, the prime motivating factor for seeking orthodontic care is parental suggestion. Orthodontics may be valued by parents for a number of reasons, including functional ones; however, sociopsychological factors, as influenced by facial form esthetics, seem to be most important. The prospective young orthodontic patient is reflective of his parents' opinions and relatively uninfluenced by peer suggestions and attitudes. Level of self-regard plays a secondary role in a child's desire for orthodontic care and is important primarily in its influence on the basic parent-child relationship. The majority of children accept parental control over orthodontic treatment decisions with the exception of those youngsters who are highly independent and unconcerned with conforming to socially dictated standards of behavior and appearance.

THE ADULT PATIENT

The prospective adult orthodontic patient, in contrast with the child, must rely primarily on self-motivation in seeking treatment. Often he is unhappy with one or more characteristics of his facial form and has first tried to alter his looks through non-professional means, i.e., change in hair style, facial cosmetics to accentuate the eyes or cheek bones, growth of a beard to strengthen the lower jaw line, or a moustache to strengthen the outline of the upper lip (Peterson, '76). However, when a facial characteristic is self-perceived as disturbing one's social interaction and acceptance, and the surface remedies are unsuccessful, an individual will often seek alternative treatment possibilities. This may be in the form of prosthetic dentistry, orthodontics, oral surgery, plastic surgery or a combination of procedures.

The increase in patient requests for orthodontic treatment and orthognathic surgery is a relatively recent occurrence. Since little attention has been given to questions of motivation in adults in previous orthodontic literature, it is necessary to turn to studies completed in plastic surgery and oral surgery to develop a classification of motives for the adult patient (Meyer et al., '60; Knorr et al., '67; Edgerton and Knorr, '71; Rozner, '73; Olley, '74a, '74b; Peterson and Topazian, '74; Reich, '75; Goin et al., '76; Laufer et al., '76; Oulette, '79). Motives can be separated into external and internal factors (Edgerton and Knorr, '71). External motivation implies input from the patients' physical and social environment, while internal motivation suggests pressures from within the patient himself. The following listing relies on this basic division of motivational pressures and describes the most frequent examples in each category.

External (Social) Pressures

1. Desire to please others and improve one's social interactions. Often this is in terms of trying to please one's spouse by looking younger or more attractive.

2. Paranoid ideation. A patient may feel that a particular aspect of his facial features causes people to be derisive towards him. The results of treatment are seen in terms of making the social environment less threatening.

3. Response to parental or significant other pressure. Family members may articulate social standards of attractiveness and reinforce the motivation for seeking corrective treatment. This is most common in younger patients.

4. Immediate crisis. A family or social problem may lead to extreme emotional reactions. In an effort to cope with these new problems, the individual may seek an appearance change (Woods, '68; Peterson and Topazian, '74).

5. Fear of being stereotyped. MacGregor ('67) calls these individuals "fixers". They want to remove a particular characteristic that identifies them with a specific religious or ethnic group or individual (Olley, '74a; Wiratmadja, '74).

6. Obstruction to a career or social ambitions. An actor may feel that an improved dental and facial appearance will help in gaining future

employment (Hollywood smile). A politician may find an esthetic dental appearance an aid to his candidacy (Linn, '66).

Internal (Self-generated) Pressures

1. Sense of personal inadequacy. A patient may express that, "I have hated this thing all my life," and finds the attribute a self-perceived block to his enjoyment of life.

2. Seekers of a new identity. MacGregor ('67) calls these people "changers". They want to change a particular facial characteristic so that they will look like somebody else, often a well known public or glamourous figure.

3. Projection of unrelated social or psychological problems onto the perceived physical abnormality. Anxieties caused by other problems are focused upon the dentofacial fault, with the individual becoming fixated on the specific anatomical characteristic (Sykes *et al.*, '72; Olley, '74*a*; Peterson and Topazian, '74; Vojdani and Horigan, '77).

4. Obsessive, insatiable desire for treatment. When some physical characteristic begins to change, an individual within this category seeks care even for the most trivial alteration. He often returns for treatment and retreatment of the same or related dentofacial problems (Knorr *et al.*, '67; Rozner, '73).

Finally, there may be no clear, self-understood motivation for seeking treatment. The patient himself may not have thought through the reasons behind his decision to obtain treatment at this particular point in his life. Goin and co-workers ('76) state that most patients who seek facial alteration are guided by sweeping hopes rather than simple desires for physical change. They conducted in-depth personality inventories and psychiatric interviews with 20 women who sought face-lift operations. During the interview sessions, the patients were encouraged to discuss their motivations for surgery. When re-interviewed post-operatively, 60% of the women gave different reasons for wanting the treatment than they had acknowledged before. While it is possible that some patients initially withheld their true motivations, it seems that, more often, the patients became aware of their true motives after secretly expected social results failed to materialize post-surgically (Table 1).

While it may be concluded that motivations for therapy of the adult patient are not always simple or obvious, it is apparent that most individuals seek corrective treatment because of sociopsychological considerations rather than functional reasons. Oullette ('78, '79) suggests that adult patients often have considered their problem for a long period of time prior to obtaining professional consultation and that they hesitated to seek care because they did not want to appear vain or because they were afraid of the financial cost of corrective care.

Table 1. Presurgical and postsurgical reports of motivation for plastic surgery of the face. (Redrawn after Goin and co-workers, 1976.)

	Before Surgery	After Surgery
Patient #1	To look better.	Your face looking younger to help you be young; society is youth oriented.
Patient #2	I need to find a new job.	I feel in competition with my 16-year-old daughter.
Patient #3	Suddenly I am falling apart and need rejuvenating.	Sometimes I fantasize that it will change my life so that I can enjoy being a "swinger".
Patient #4	My husband is retiring and I don't want to stay home and grow old.	I had hoped that my husband would become more potent. He didn't.
Patient #5	To get rid of my aged look.	I did it to get my husband to mother me. It didn't work.
Patient #6	I wanted to regain my pride in my appearance.	I didn't tell you before. I did it to help me get a new job.

THE INFLUENCE OF PERSONALITY CHARACTERISTICS ON SUCCESS OF TREATMENT

Having recognized the diversity of motivational patterns that lead to corrective orthodontic treatment or orthognathic surgery, it must be assumed that patient management has to be tailored to the sociopsychological needs of the individual (Fisk, '63; Allen and Hodgson, '68; Krajicek, '69a, '69b; Pierce, '71; Belmont, '73). This is most important when a major dentofacial change is to be a part of therapy. When the patient is an adult, the clinician must thoroughly understand the patient's motivations and expectations *before* treatment is begun in order to assure patient satisfaction when the treatment has been completed. For the child patient, the situation is much different. The parent is usually the motivating factor for treatment, but it is the child's personality characteristics that will determine how he/she reacts to wearing appliances and, therefore, the ultimate success of corrective therapy. The following discussion reviews the important psychosocial patient characteristics that influence both the self-perceived social and functional success of orthodontic therapy.

The Adult Patient

Satisfaction with results of treatment are closely related to the patient's understanding of the problem prior to the initiation of any treatment. Does the patient have a realistic idea of what he wants from treatment (Woods, '68; Spater *et al.*, '71; Rozner, '73; Reich, '75)? Jensen ('78) has suggested that there are three psychosocial areas that must be evaluated to assess the possibilities for success in any treatment that alters dentofacial form.

First, there must be a consideration of the defect itself. Is the defect readily noticeable, or is it overly magnified in the patient's self-evaluation in comparison to social and cultural norms (MacGregor, '51; Woods, '68; Nicoletis, '72; Vojdani and Horigan, '77)? The nature of the defect, i.e., whether it is acquired or developmental, is important. Congenital defects or long-term problems in growth and development lend themselves to better post-treatment satisfaction than do traumatic or recently induced injuries (Edgerton and Knorr, '71; Peterson and Topazian, '74). The individual who suffers from a traumatic injury often expects treatment to return them to normal, which often is an unrealistic objective. On the other hand, the individual with a developmental problem (the type most often seen in an orthodontist's office) has not experienced "normality", so any improvement is much more appreciated.

Second, there must be an evaluation of the social (external) factors that have motivated the patient to seek treatment. If the motivating factor is to please another member of the family or a friend, the clinician must consider what the likelihood is that the family and close social contacts will be supportive of treatment-induced facial form changes after therapy is completed (Olley, '74*b*; Reich, '75). A patient who is unhappy about a particular aspect of his visage may not be completely satisfied post-treatment even when the offending aspect has been corrected (Chasens, '72; Newman, '78). Long-term acquaintances are not likely to change their relationship with an individual as a result of cosmetic facial change alone. However, if other post-treatment changes occur, such as changes in personality that result in more self-confidence, then there is often post-operative improvement in social interaction (Rozner, '73).

Corrective orthodontic treatment or orthognathic surgery may be helpful for patients who seek treatment because they feel a particular dentofacial characteristic is obstructive to their career or social ambitions, but the clinician must be careful that the patient does not expect too much from treatment. For example, the young patient who wants a "Hollywood smile" for an acting career, but who lacks the talent for acting, may be disappointed in the treatment result (Edgerton and Knorr, '71).

Finally, there must be an evaluation of psychological motivating factors. The well-adjusted individual, whose feelings about his dentofacial abnormality are commensurate with its objective importance, is most likely to be satisfied with therapy (Hay, '70; Peterson and Topazian, '74; Jensen, '78). Self-acknowledged dislike of a particular characteristic, as long as the individual does not project unrelated social or psychological problems onto the defect (Woods, '68; Bailey and Edwards, '75), is a valid reason for seeking corrective treatment. Patients whose desires for treatment are obsessive, or whose expectations of themselves or of the practitioner are irrational, usually have deep-seated psychological problems that require management by a clinical psychologist or psychiatrist. The patient who complains of previous "disappointing experiences" or "bad treatment" from other dental, surgical or mental health professionals may exhibit this type of problem (MacGregor et al., '53; Knorr et al., '67; Olley, '74a; Rozner, '73; Jensen, '78).

As a rule, external or social motivations for treatment are less desirable, as they usually reflect the results expected by family, friends or work associates, rather than those expected by the clinician. Internal or psychological factors are usually the result of long-term deliberations by the patient, with the patient having a more realistic view of what is to be expected as a result of treatment. The expected results are centered on *self* change and, therefore, are more likely to be satisfactory (Peterson and Topazian, '74).

For most mature, adult patients, a pre-treatment, factual discussion of the patient's motivations for therapy, the time involved, and the type of appliance that is necessary (Formicola and Binder, '72), along with a realistic evaluation of the projected physical and social results of treatment, will preclude dissatisfaction with treatment results.

The Child Patient

The young patient enters the clinical office usually at the behest of his parents, rather than by his own choice. While his motivations for orthodontic treatment may be reflective of his parents' views, it is often necessary to instill some degree of personal identification with the orthodontic problem in order to elicit the requisite amount of patient cooperation. An adult makes his own decision to seek care, usually is financially responsible for that care, and is essentially self-motivated, all of which leads to a high degree of cooperation during treatment. Usually, a child neither initiates treatment nor is financially responsible for it, which can jeopardize treatment if the child is not highly motivated to cooperate with the clinician (Zadok, '65; Eastwood, '78; Graber, '79).

The Timing of Orthodontic Treatment. Weiss and Eiser ('77), in a study of 274 patients, stated that from a psychological standpoint, orthodontic treatment that required the wear of removable appliances (headgear, activator, etc.) should be completed before the onset of puberty. Changing physical and psychosocial interactions which normally occur during the adolescent period combine to reduce the responsiveness of the patient to the doctor's requests for cooperation. Jacobson ('79) also noted that early treatment is psychologically advantageous to children whose self-image has been affected by peer group teasing. In general, treatment timing must be tempered by the psychological and emotional development of the child patient, in which case some youngsters will be able to receive treatment at an earlier chronological age than others (Maj *et al.*, '67; Colenaty and Gabriel, '77).

Allan and Hodgson ('68) reported that age was the best predictor of patient cooperation (r=.51). In a study that utilized the Maryland Parent Attitude Survey and Adjective Check List, they developed a composite picture of the cooperative—versus the uncooperative—patient. The cooperative child is fourteen years or younger, enthusiastic, outgoing, energetic, wholesome, self-controlled, responsible, trusting, hardworking, forthright and obliging to others. The uncooperative patient is more than fourteen years of age, hard-headed, independent, superior in intellect, aloof, often nervous, temperamental, individualistic, and tends to disregard the wishes of others. These findings are consistent with those of Kreit and colleagues ('68) whose personality inventory indicated that the cooperative child has conforming attitudes and a good parent-child relationship. In the earlier discussion of motivation for orthodontic therapy, it was noted that the parents' views are reflected in the child's desire for treatment (Baldwin and Barnes, '65, '66; Warford, '73), except for those children who were exceedingly independent (Virolainen, '67; Lewit and Virolainen, '68). Hence, it appears that motivation for treatment and several specific personality factors are closely related to child-patient cooperation.

The Difficult Child. Although it seems that from a sociopsychological standpoint the best age to treat patients is in the pre-pubertal age range, in reality, most patients seen in an orthodontist's office are teenagers. It is at this point in their social development that they are the most combative and questioning of authority (Erikson, '68; Jersild, '68; McCandless, '70). This fact, along with the general authoritarian nature of most clinicians, primes the doctor-patient relationship for strife rather than cooperation (Weiss and Eiser, '77; Miller and Larson, '79).

Miller and Larson ('79), in an excellent analysis of the unsuccessful orthodontist-adolescent patient relationship, have suggested that there may be four reasons why some patients are exceedingly unresponsive to the clinician's ministrations. First, the orthodontist is frequently a casualty of the natural parent-child conflict. The young adult at this stage desires to have more control over his own destiny (including his physical development) and resents the parent's demand that he "submit" to orthodontic treatment. Another facet of this problem is that the clinician may be seen as an alternate parental figure, complicating the relationship even further (Joshi and Prokash, '78).

The second reason is related to the psychological importance of the mouth. As Belmont ('73) states, "The mouth is a repository of dynamic, genetic, developmental, maturational and emotional components, hardly a static and controlled working milieu." The placement of appliances may be viewed by the adolescent as an invasion of his own body, with resultant negative feelings toward the clinician. Additionally, any discomfort may be psychologically amplified because of the special emotional sensitivity of this area.

The third reason is the unesthetic character of orthodontic appliances. For some youngsters, teasing about the wearing of appliances (particularly if they are older teens) will induce strong negative attitudes toward the "braces". Other youngsters may actually value their appliances as a mark of high socioeconomic status, a fact that leads some teenagers to request appliances even though no dental problem exists.

Finally, Miller and Larson note that some youngsters have a very negative image of themselves. These children feel that their unattractive dentofacial form is part of their overall make-up and is unchangeable. Indeed, they do not want to look better because they feel themselves to be basically unattractive. External cosmetic change is seen as an unwanted assault on the individual's negative self-concept. This negativism is an overall problem of personality development and really has little to do with the dentofacial areas.

The basic difference between the compliant and non-compliant patient can be reduced to a question of authority. Using a specially designed attitudinal test survey, Miller and Larson ('79) reported that, for ninety patients, there was a significant correlation between attitude toward authority and compliance in orthodontic care. Additionally, it was noted that males demonstrated a significantly higher concern over the invasive nature of intraoral appliances than did females and that boys were actively more aggressive towards authority than were the girls (a finding supported in the general psychology literature—see Lerner et al., '76, for example). These findings, along with a greater concern evidenced by females over facial appearance, are supportive of empirical statements that girls make better orthodontic patients than boys.

Patient management for the child who is hostile toward authority requires a different treatment approach by the clinician. Suggestions such as, "If you don't wear your headgear I'll tie it in" or "You should brush your teeth better—just think of all the money your parents are wasting on you" are bound to engender increased negativism toward treatment. It is important to explain the *clinical* necessity of treatment as distinct from parental pressures to have appliances placed. The patient must personally identify with the treatment and develop an appreciation for the functional and esthetic goals of therapy (Gabriel, '68; Moore, '72; Clemmer and Hayes, '79). This approach to patient motivation (i.e., the personalization of treatment goals for the youngster) has met with particular success in orthodontic dental plaque control programs (Gold, '75; Clark, '76; Schwaninger and Vickers-Schwaninger, '79) and is bound to increase the chances for obtaining successful treatment results with non-compliant patients (Belmont, '73; Miller and Larson, '79).

SELF-PERCEPTION AND EVALUATION OF DENTAL AND FACIAL FORM

Although it appears that individuals can identify deviations from normal facial form in other individuals from an early age (Lucker, this volume), when they are asked to evaluate their own dentofacial type, their perceptions are far from accurate. In studies of general body type, it has been demonstrated that individuals who are physically unattractive by societal standards tend to view themselves as being more attractive than they are actually judged to be (Schonbu and Chell, '67; Cremer and Hukill, '69; Bailey *et al.*, '70; Gellert *et al.*, '71; Minihan, '71). As the facial region is more visible and identifiable to the individual than is his general body form, it is important to evaluate how well a person can judge his own facial characteristics and how this evaluation correlates with satisfaction with his appearance.

Studies that have evaluated self-perception of dental characteristics indicate that people are generally aware of dentofacial abnormalities, particularly excessive overjet (sticking out of the upper front teeth) or lower tooth crowding. With increased severity of the problem (as judged objectively by a clinician), there is an increasing level of self-recognition (Howitt *et al.*, '67; Lewit and Virolainen, '68; Ingervall and Hedegaard, '74; Drake, '77). Ingervall and Hedegaard ('74) suggest that for boys in their late teens, mandibular (lower jaw) tooth crowding was the most salient feature in terms of malocclusion, even when compared to perceptions of overjet. They also reported that anomalies in the front of the mouth (i.e., missing teeth, rotations, discolorations, crowding, etc.) are much more influential in self-perceptions of dental attractiveness than problems in the posterior dental segments.

96

As is true for evaluation of general body attractiveness, those who are less dentally and facially attractive are more likely to be mistaken in their self-evaluations. Lewit and Virolainen ('68) and Pitt and Korabik ('77) reported a .45 correlation between self-perception and actual, clinical evaluations of dentofacial form. It seems that part of the reason for the relatively low correlation is that individuals with more severe dentofacial form abnormalities evaluated themselves more favorably than their situation warranted. This finding is corroborated by the work of Horowitz and co-workers ('71), who reported that when youngsters were asked to match their own profile with line drawings of other children, those children who deviated most from normal facial form selected matches that were significantly more normal than their own. In a similar study, in which women were asked to select both an ideal profile type and one that matched their own facial outline, it was found that the women underestimated their own less desirable characteristics and selected outlines highly correlated to their "most desired" profile type (Giddon et al., '74). It would appear that unattractive dentofacial attributes are ignored to some degree while more desirable facial characteristics are stressed, particularly by those individuals with more severe imbalances of facial form.

It was these earlier studies and an interest in the underlying considerations of facial form self-evaluation and attractiveness self-satisfaction that led to our own large-scale study, conducted in three different school systems in southeastern Michigan. This research involved a sample of over 600 children, of which a subset (264 Caucasian females, 217 males) were tested fully on self-evaluation and satisfaction with facial form. The entire subject group was characterized as predominantly middle class with a large representation of blue-collar families.

Data for this study were collected in two separate visits to the classrooms of the children. During the first visit, the children answered a series of questionnaires on physical- and self-esteem, including questions on self-evaluation and satisfaction with their dental and facial attractiveness. At a second visit, a different testing team made comprehensive orthodontic and dental esthetic evaluations of the children.

The questions used in the self-evaluation segment were designed to (1) assess the subjects' ability to recognize the presence or absence of malocclusion, (2) assess the subjects' tendency to transfer the evaluation of his own appearance to an esthetic scale, (3) correlate subjective satisfaction with objective measures of dentofacial form, and (4) assess the subjects' transference of dental esthetics to facial esthetics. Although the subjects were given a 5-point scale during the testing sequence, the answers were grouped into three categories, i.e., negative, neutral and positive, for purposes of statistical evaluation.

The distribution of answers to the five questions asked in this section of

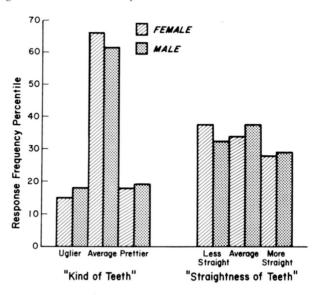

Figure 2. Response frequency distribution to self-evaluative questions.

the test are illustrated in Figures 2 through 4. There was no statistical difference in the distribution for males and females, although values for both are pictured. In the first question, which asked for an evaluation of the straightness of the teeth (Fig. 2), there was a fairly even division among the answers of the respondents. When their responses were correlated with objective dental measures taken by an orthodontic specialist, it was found that the subjects made fairly accurate self-evaluations. Measurements for overjet (sticking out of upper front teeth) and lower incisor crowding were significantly related at the .01 level or better. Thus, it appears that the subjects made a realistic appraisal of their anatomic condition.

In the second question, the subjects were asked to evaluate dentofacial esthetics by choosing what kind of teeth they had. There were five choices available, ranging from pretty to ugly. As shown in Figure 2, 60% of the children felt their teeth were about the same as their peers', while 20% felt they were better looking, and 16% felt they were uglier than average. The variability in frequency response between the previous question and this one illustrates the difference between an item that asks for a realistic appraisal (straightness) versus one that asks for an esthetic judgment. It may be assumed that the criteria for straightness of teeth are better defined than the socially encumbered decision on esthetics. Again, however, the evaluations of overjet and lower tooth crowding were significantly related to the esthetic judgments for both males (p< .01) and females (p< .05).

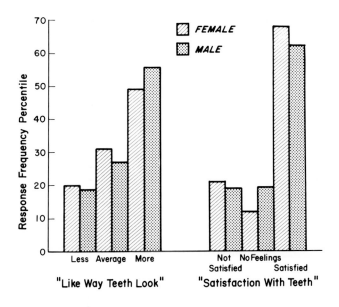

Figure 3. Response frequency distribution to self-satisfaction questions.

The two questions that analyzed the subject's self-satisfaction (Fig. 3) showed a distinct positive bias, with only 20% of the respondents reporting negative feelings toward their teeth. While statistically significant relationships were found at the .05 level between self-satisfaction and overjet in females and mandibular crowding in males, it is likely that there were other factors that were more important in deciding satisfaction than the dental esthetic variables that were tested (see discussion below on self-esteem and self-satisfaction). These low level correlations between objective dental measures and self-satisfaction are in agreement with the previous report of Howitt and co-workers ('67).

The final question assessed the transference from dental esthetic judgments to facial esthetic judgments. Again, there was a very strong positive bias in the answers of the entire sample, with over 55% of the group indicating that they felt that their teeth helped improve their overall facial appearance (Fig. 4). An interesting sex difference was noted when comparisons were made between the subject's response and his/her objective dental measures. For females, *overjet* was significantly related at the .001 level to their decision on whether or not they liked their teeth. Those girls whose upper teeth were more protruding felt that their teeth were a negative factor in their overall facial attractiveness. For males, on the other hand, *lower tooth crowding* was related at the .01 level to their decision on how their teeth influenced facial esthetics.

It can be postulated that the females made a more direct transfer of

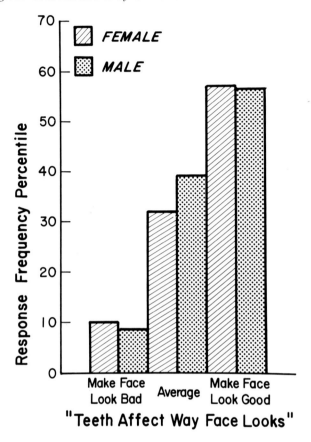

Figure 4. Response frequency distribution to dental effect on facial appearance question.

their dental condition to their overall facial esthetics, since increases in overjet are responsible for altered lip posture and facial form. Facial attractiveness, per se, is more salient for females than males (Lerner and Moore, '74; Simmons and Rosenberg, '75), and dental abnormalities which alter the facial form are thus more strongly perceived by the female population. The males, whose facial esthetic criteria are less well established, focused on the more localized esthetic problem of dental crowding.

INFLUENCE OF ONE'S OWN PHYSICAL FORM ON PERCEPTION OF OTHERS

Little research has been carried out on this aspect of person perception. The work which has been conducted on general body form has produced equivocal results. Caskey and Felker ('71), for example, reported that body type does not influence one's stereotyping of attributes to other people. Yet, studies that correlated perceiver body build with judgments of peer physique noted that youngsters with thin or average builds were more accurate judges than children who were overweight (Lerner and Gellert, '69). These authors suggest that the condition of overweight was a salient feature in self-evaluation and, hence, was also important in the evaluation of others.

Research results in the dentofacial literature are equally problematic. Drake ('77) reported that neither a person's sex nor presence of a malocclusion had any effect on his/her perception of the facial types of others. On the other hand, studies by Virolainen ('67), on an almost identical sample, reported that females were more perceptive than males and that increasing severity of perceiver malocclusion resulted in increased recognition of dentofacial abnormalities. The literature on stigmata tends to support this latter finding. Goffman ('63) reports that an individual who possesses a trait that can readily be identified as being different from his peers is more likely to note that trait in other individuals. He states that even relatively minor deviations from normal form are often self-perceived as being abberant and, as a result, are over-valued in the perception of self as well as in the perception of others.

To better test this postulate, 212 ten- to twelve-year-old students were asked to view a series of photographs of a group of same-aged children who represented differing types of dentofacial form and who had been previously classified in terms of the Angle system. The students selected for this project were unaware that the real purpose of the study was to evaluate their abilities at perception of differing facial form types. They were prompted with written and orally presented instructions that asked them to note whether there was "something wrong" or "nothing wrong" with the pictured individuals' facial appearances. After the children had viewed all the photographs, they were given a dental examination that established their own dentofacial classification according to the Angle system. Figure 5 depicts the differences in judgments of normality between the subjects who were classified as being Class II (retruded lower jaw—protruded upper jaw) or Class I (normal jaw-to-jaw relationship). It can easily be seen that those youngsters who had a malocclusion themselves gave lower scores to the pictures than the youngsters with normal facial form. This relationship (significant at .001 level) appears to support the contention that the presence of an abnormality in facial form by the perceiver influences his judgments of other individuals.

SELF-ESTEEM AND DENTOFACIAL FORM

Other papers in this volume by Adams and by Berscheid have addressed the correlation between general physical attractiveness and self-

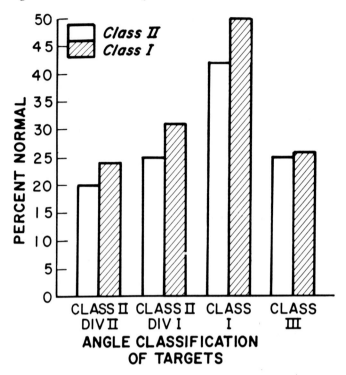

Figure 5. Normality judgments of targets differentiated on basis of subject's own malocclusion classification. Class I (normal) subjects were significantly more lenient in their evaluations of the target group than were the Class II subjects.

esteem. They have demonstrated that physical attractiveness is an important parameter for social development for both males and females. For females, attractiveness is seen in terms of physical form while for males, effectiveness of physical type is socially more important. This leads to a different operational definition of what attractiveness means for males and females (Lerner and Korn, '72; Dion and Berscheid, '74; Lerner *et al.*, '76; Mahoney and Finch, '76).

Body image and self-esteem are certainly well correlated. There are, however, many components of the self-concept that, depending on their importance to the individual in question, control overall self-regard. Rosenberg ('75) stated that, in addition to a general social identity, there are an endless number of dispositions and characteristics (kindness, honesty, generosity, intelligence, physical form), as well as a variety of ego-extensions (parents, children, created works). Each of the parts of the self-concept is valued and judged (positively or negatively) to varying—but *individual*—degrees. Hence, the person who has an abnormality of facial form may be well aware of it, but he is also aware of his other characteristics. The relative value he gives his deformity, as well as the severity of his feelings, will decide how much his overall self-esteem is affected. (For an in-depth review of coping mechanisms, see Goffman, '63). By the same token, the overall strength of an individual's self-concept will serve to dampen the effects of one particular component of the self-concept when that characteristic is incongruent with the others.

Influence of Self-Esteem on Self Satisfaction With Dental Appearance

Previous discussion in this paper demonstrated that perception of either the presence or absence of dentofacial abnormality was usually accurate. The greater the severity of a malocclusion, the more accurate the judgment. Yet, there are situations where people with definite malocclusions are not dissatisfied or where individuals with good occlusion report dissatisfaction (Frazier and Lisonbee, '50; Baldwin and Barnes, '65; Howitt *et al.*, '67; Virolainen, '67; Hilzenrath and Baldwin, '71; Drake, '77). Indeed, it has also been reported that individuals who possess a particular type of malocclusion are more likely to rate that type more favorably than would the average individual (Cohen and Horowitz, '70). While self-satisfaction with teeth and objective evaluations of dentofacial form are somewhat correlated, there are other factors, i.e., psychological aspects, that are superimposed on the satisfaction decision (Allen and Hodgson, '68; Woods, '68; Stricker, '70; Weiss and Eiser, '77; Miller and Larson, '79). The psychological factors include various aspects of the self-concept that may be totally unrelated to facial characteristics.

In order to examine the relationship of self-concept with the self-evaluation and self-satisfaction decisions, the children participating in the school system study (reported earlier in this paper) were also given the Piers-Harris Children's Self Concept Scale (Piers, '69). This is a widely used self-esteem scale for children in the age group evaluated (see Robinson and Shaver, '73, for in-depth analysis of this scale). The first question the students were asked in the earlier study was how straight their teeth were. Their answers correlated highly with objective measures of dentofacial form. Figure 6 illustrates that there was no significant difference between groups of respondents on the basis of overall self-esteem. Hence, these results would tend to support the contention that individuals are able to make objective analyses of their anatomical condition.

The second question asked for an esthetic evaluation of the teeth, i.e., what kind of teeth (pretty-ugly) the individual perceived he had. The majority of subjects responded that they had average teeth. As reported above, however, the statistical strength of the relationship between the self-judgments and objective dental-esthetic measures was lower for this

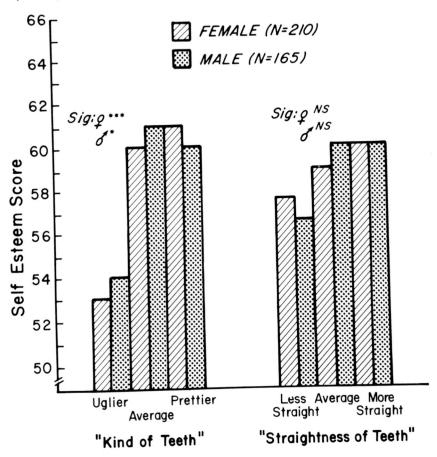

Figure 6. Self-esteem scores for self-evaluative groupings. Statistical significance levels for one-way analysis of variance are indicated for male and female subjects.

question than in the straightness question. Figure 6 demonstrates that for this esthetic self-evaluation, overall self-esteem was strongly related to the judgment, especially for females. One may suggest that the ugly-beauty dichotomy was more salient for females, hence the greater relationship in this parameter when compared to that of the males.

In answer to the questions that assessed satisfaction with the teeth, only 20% of the sample indicated that either they didn't like the way their teeth looked or were not satisfied with their teeth. Only low level correlations were found between the objective dental-esthetic measures and the self-satisfaction judgments, particulary for males. Figure 7 depicts the relationship between the self-judgments of the subjects and their objec-

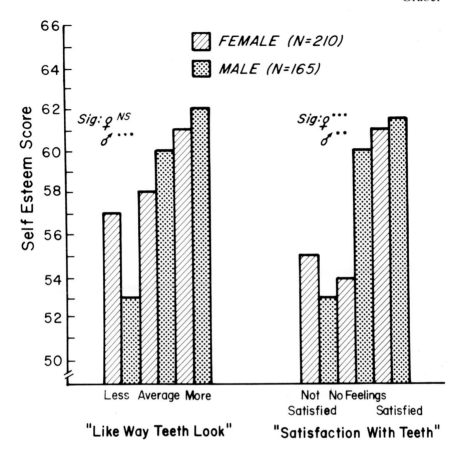

Figure 7. Self-esteem scores for self-satisfaction groupings. Statistical significance for one-way analysis of variance are indicated for male and female subjects.

tive self-esteem scores. For males, it can be observed that for both questions there is a highly significant relationship between overall self-esteem and the dental esthetic satisfaction judgment. The males did not seem to differentiate between these two questions, and those with low self-concept were more likely to answer negatively in self-judgment, while those with high self-esteem gave average or above average self-evaluations. The data for the females is more difficult to decipher. It appears that girls separated the "like teeth" from the satisfaction question, i.e., one may not "like" the way her teeth look from an objective level (objective dental measures of overjet were correlated at the .05 level with self-judgments on this item) but may still be satisfied with them because the dental esthetic judgment is not important to the individual. Hence, there was no statistically different response to the "liking" question between the three self-judgment groups on the basis of self-concept. On the other hand, the "satisfaction" response was strongly related to the self-concept measure, with those individuals who were "satisfied" scoring significantly higher in the self-esteem than those girls who reported no feelings either way or feelings of not being satisfied. These findings substantiate the work of Pitt and Korabik ('77) who suggested that self-satisfaction with dental characteristics is controlled by self-esteem. It may be postulated that the sex difference in the responses to these questions is due to the differential experience in self-evaluation of dentofacial characteristics, i.e., the girls being more concerned with facial cosmetics than the boys.

The final question in the earlier study was in regard to how the teeth affect facial looks. The answers showed that for females there was a very significant relationship between objective measures of excessive overjet and self-evaluations, indicating that maloccluded teeth were a negative esthetic attribute. A little over 10% of the female subjects had excessive overjet. It is then most interesting to see (Fig. 8) that the self-concept scores of these individuals fall significantly below those of individuals who judged themselves to be average or above average dentoesthetically. While one must be careful in drawing conclusions as to causal relationships from the data presented here, it may be postulated that those girls who had excessive amounts of overjet also had altered facial form esthetics. This abnormality was (1) perceived and objectively evaluated, (2) valued as an important physical characteristic, and (3) had some influence on overall self-judgment.

For males, the only dental-esthetic objective measure to be related to the teeth-affect-face self-judgment was lower front tooth crowding, which was statistically significant at the .01 level. Lower tooth crowding is primarily a local esthetic factor and has little effect on overall facial form. Figure 8 indicates, however, a very strong relationship between the male subgroup, which gave negative dental-esthetic self-judgments, and their self-esteem (significant at .0001 level). It appears that, although lower tooth crowding may provide some focus on this dentally related question, the more primary controlling factor for the response is overall self-esteem. Hence, for the males, this dentofacial abnormality was perceived and objectively evaluated, but it was probably not the dominant factor in making dentofacial self-judgments.

It would appear from the data presented here that in matters of self-evaluation, both males and females can and do make objective evaluations of their own anatomical facial form. For males, responses to questions on satisfaction with dentofacial esthetics are strongly mediated by overall self-esteem. For females, the picture is more complex. Overall self-esteem is usually a major determinant of decisions on satisfaction

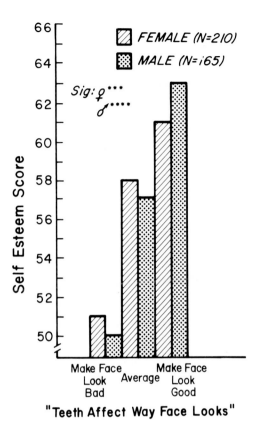

Figure 8. Self-esteem scores for self-groupings of dental effect on facial appearance. Statistical significance levels are indicated for male and female subjects.

with one's teeth. However, for those girls who have excessive amounts of overjet resulting in facial form distortion, self-esteem appears to be negatively influenced by the dentofacial abnormality.

Influence of Dentofacial Form on Self Esteem

Most reports correlating self-concept with malocclusion have been characterized by a case report format with little support for extrapolation to the general population (Pierce, '71). Yet, this literature forms the basis of much of the current orthodontic and surgical professional opinion on the relationship between altered facial form and self-image. Exemplary of these early reports are discussions by Root ('49), Epstein ('58) and Picard ('64), who suggest that an individual with a self-perceived facial form abnormality will develop feelings of shame and inferiority.

107

Work with cleft lip and palate children has shown, however, that severity of an orofacial form problem is not always correlated to the degree of self-concept alteration. There is often little personality difference between cleft and non-cleft individuals (Watson, '64; Reuss, '65, '67; Schweckendiek, '70; Clifford *et al.*, 1972). Clifford ('67) and others (MacGregor, '53; Wirls, '71; Tisza and Gumpertz, '73) have suggested that individuals with obvious abnormalities often have assimilated their condition into their total self-regard and value it as only a minor component in the self-esteem construct. Hence, the child who is obviously deformed learns to accept the deformity and the reactions of family and society to it (MacGregor, '53).

The child who has a minor form distortion, such as a common malocclusion, may perceive the problem to be worse and may harbor more concern than the anatomical abnormality warrants. His coping mechanisms may not be as well developed as the individual who is obviously deformed, and he may be overly anxious due to his uncertainty over familial or societal responses to the perceived problem (Hay, '70; MacGregor, '70). These concerns are often well founded. As MacGregor notes, " . . . the person with buck teeth is less likely to be looked at with compassion than as a target for nicknaming and stereotyping."

Recent reports (Dennington, '75; Murphy, '76) indicate that the patient who seeks orthodontic treatment has a more negative feeling toward his teeth than non-patients. This finding certainly is in line with the work on patient motivation discussed earlier in this paper. However, attempts to correlate objective dental measures with overall self-esteem have produced equivocal results. Dennington ('75) and Murphy ('76) found only low correlations between self-esteem and dental measures and Klima and co-workers ('75, '79) found a relationship between self-esteem and dental measures in only Class III individuals (lower jaw protrudes beyond upper jaw). Methodological variabilities between these studies make it difficult to compare them. In addition, the majority of studies of correlation between objective dental measures and overall self-esteem have been completed on dental school clinic samples, which raises questions about the validity of these findings for the population in general.

Another inherent problem in this type of research is the complexity of the face as a signal of "abnormality". The component parts are so varied and interact in so many combinations that it is very difficult to make generalizations about the relationship between objective measures of facial form and self-esteem, unless those dental esthetic measures are of the most gross type. Specific characteristics may look good in one facial construct and be completely unacceptable in another. Data from the sample of school children reported here does show a trend in the relationship between the Angle dental classification and self-concept (Fig. 9). As has

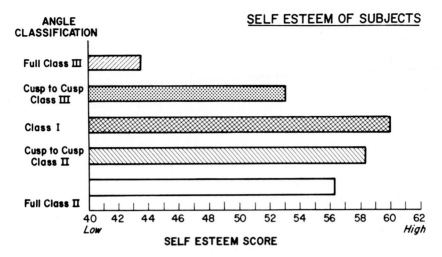

ANGLE
CLASSIFICATION

SELF ESTEEM OF SUBJECTS

SELF ESTEEM SCORE

Figure 9. Self-esteem scores of 175 ten to thirteen-year-old Caucasian school children, reported on the basis of their own Angle dental classification. These scores, taken from one school system, indicate a tendency toward reduced self-esteem with increasing dentofacial distortion, as measured by the Angle classification. Class III subjects, in particular, show significantly reduced self-esteem scores relative to Class I (normal) and Class II youngsters.

been reported by Klima and co-workers ('75, '79), those individuals with a Class III, protruding lower jaw have, as a group, lower self-esteem. It also appears that self-esteem diminishes somewhat with increasing Class II (protruding upper jaw) characteristics. Yet, one would have to exercise much caution in applying this generalized finding to the specific, prospective orthodontic patient. The graphic representations reflect mean scores, and large variances indicate that there are individual-specific variables that contribute to the importance of this dentofacial form variable.

Consideration of past research, along with the work presented here, suggests that there is a complex interaction between dentofacial form and overall self-esteem. The first variable to be considered is the level of overall self-esteem of the subject himself. When self-esteem is low before treatment, alterations in facial esthetics are more likely to have an important psychological impact than when self-esteem is already high before treatment begins. The second variable to look at is the location and degree of the deformity. Alterations that are proximal to the dental region and cause distortion of balanced facial form close to the communicative zones are more likely to result in changes in self-esteem than those that are more distant from the mouth and have less effect on the soft tissue facial contours. Major facial form deformities (e.g., cleft lip) are likely to evoke special coping mechanisms that protect self-esteem, while more minor, self-perceived facial form disproportions (e.g., malocclusion) may produce anxieties with resultant changes in self-esteem. The final variable of import is the differential importance of esthetics between males and females, i.e., the sex factor. Females value good facial esthetics more highly in their self-esteem constructs than do males. Hence, most dentofacial disproportions are more significant to overall self-esteem of females than they are for males.

POST-TREATMENT PSYCHOLOGICAL CHANGE

Psychological changes following facial form change are considered in detail elsewhere in this volume (see papers by Munro and Redmond). Therefore, only brief consideration is given here. There is abundant anecdotal literature that suggests that most patients are satisfied with the esthetic correction they obtain following orthodontic or orthognathic surgical treatment (Meerloo, '56; Blausten, '73; Myrberg and Thilander, '73; Oullette, '78, '79). Studies in which patients are questioned as to their own perceptions of improved self-esteem suggest most individuals feel that their self-confidence has improved along with their improved appearance (Hutton, '67; Crowel *et al.*, '70; Schroeder, '72; Sims, '72; Weiss, '73; Laufer *et al.*, '76; Fukaya, '78; Oullette, '79). Of more scientific value than self-report studies are the scaled measures of self-esteem recorded during and after treatment. Dennington ('75) has reported that the mere placement of orthodontic appliances results in improved self-esteem. This may be the patient's reaction to his expectations of improved cosmetic appearance.

Although there are some studies to the contrary (Meyer *et al.*, '73; Rutzen, '73), the majority of authors suggest that treatment positively influences body image and self-esteem (Story, '66; Stricker, '70). Treated individuals tend to have improvements in associated personality characteristics. For example, it has been found that individuals with treated malocclusions compared to their untreated counterparts have higher levels of achievement motivation. (Hilzenrath and Baldwin, '70). Reports have also indicated that treatment induced alterations in facial esthetics may improve the recidivism rate in deformed delinquent individuals (Meyer *et al.*, '73). Attributional studies suggest that the treated individual receives positive social support from other individuals that did not occur during his/her pre-treatment situation (Merrifield, '76). It appears that treated individuals not only subjectively see themselves as being more attractive, but also receive objective support from the surrounding society.

In summary, treatment regimens that improve facial appearance appear to have concomitant improvements in esthetic self-satisfaction and body image. More precise research is required in this area to define those changes which contribute most to improved self-esteem. Furthermore, the influence of patient age and sex requires more complete evaluation. While there is still much work required in the evaluation of post-treatment patients, it can be stated that, for the most part, treatment-induced improvements in facial esthetics result in associated improvements in self-esteem.

REFERENCES

Allen T. K. and E. W. Hodgson. The use of personality measurements as a determinant of patient cooperation in an orthodontic practice. Am. J. Orthodont. 54(6):433-440, 1968.

Bailey, L. W. and D. Edwards. Psychological considerations in maxillofacial prosthetics. J. Pros. Dent. 34:533-538, 1975.

Bailey, W. L., M. M. Shinedling and I. R. Payne. Obese individuals' perception of body image. Percept. Mot. Skills, 31(2):617-618, 1970.

Baldwin, D. C. and M. L. Barnes. Patterns of motivation in families seeking orthodontic treatment. J. Dent. Res. 45:412, 1966.

Baldwin, D.C. and M. L. Barnes. Psychosocial factors motivating orthodontic treatment. J. Dent. Res. 44:461, 1965.

Bemart, H. S. Child psychiatry and orthodontic problems. J. Oral Med. 28(2):47-53, 1973.

Belmont, H. S. Child psychiatry and orthodontic problems. J. Oral Med. 28(2):47-53, 1973.

Bialer, I. Conceptualization of success and failure in mentally retarded and normal children. J. Personal. 29:303-302, 1961.

Blausten, S. Preventing and correcting personality problems with timely treatment. Dent. Surv. J. Dent. Pract. 49:59-61, 1973.

Caskey, S. R. and D. W. Felker. Social stereotyping of female body image by elementary school age girls. Res. Q. Am. Assoc. Health Phys. Ed. 42(3):251-255, 1971.

Chasens, A. I. Indications and contraindications for adult tooth movement. Dent. Clin. N. Am. 16:423-437, 1972.

Clark, J. R. Oral hygiene in the orthodontic practice: Motivation responsibilities and concepts. Am. J. Orthodont. 69:72-82, 1976.

Clemmer, E. J. and E. W. Hayes. Patient cooperation in wearing orthodontic headgear. Am. J. Orthodont. 75:517-524, 1979.

Clifford, E. Connotative meaning of concepts related to cleft lip and palate. Cleft Pal. J. 4:165-169, 1967.

Clifford, E., E. C. Crocker and B. A. Pope. Psychological findings in the adulthood of 88 cleft-lip/palate children. Plast. Reconstr. Surg. 50(3):234-237, 1972.

Cohen, L. Social psychological factors associated with malocclusion. Internatl. Dent. J. 20:643-653, 1970.

Cohen, L. and H. S. Horowitz. Occlusal relations in children born and reared in an optionally flouridated community. III. Social-psychological findings. Angle Orthodont. 40:159-169, 1970.

Colenaty, C. and H. F. Gabriel. Predicting patient cooperation. J. Clin. Orthodont. *11*:814-819, 1977.

Crandall, V. C., V. J. Crandall and W. Katkovsky. A children's social desirability questionnaire. J. Consult. Psych. *29*:27-36, 1965.

Cremer, A. G. and M. A. Hukill. Relationships between weight-height ratios, other body measurements and self-perception of body contours. Res. Q. Am. Assoc. Health Phys. Ed. *40*(1):30-38, 1969.

Crowell, N. T., H. J. Sazima and S. T. Elder. Survey of patients' attitudes after surgical correction of prognathism: Study of 33 patients. J. Oral Surg. *28*:818-822, 1970.

Dennington, R. J. The self concept of seventy-seven orthodontic patients treated at St. Louis University. Master's Thesis, St. Louis University, 1975.

Dion, K. K. and E. Berscheid. Physical attractiveness and peer perception. Sociometry, *37*:1-12, 1974.

Drake, D. G. Teenage perceptions, degree of self-awareness, and attitudes concerning malocclusion. Master's Thesis. University of Michigan, Ann Arbor, 1977.

Eastwood, A. W. The monoblock appliance. Dent. Clin. N. Am. *22*:739-755, 1978.

Edgerton, M. T.,and N. J. Knorr. Motivational patterns of patients seeking cosmetic (esthetic) surgery. J. Plast. Reconstr. Surg. *48*:551-557, 1971.

Epstein, C. M. Psychological impact of facial deformity. Am. J. Surg. *96*:747-748, 1958.

Erikson, E. H. *Identity: Youth and Crisis*. Norton, New York, 1968.

Fisk, R. O. Physiological and sociopsychological significance of malocclusion. Can. Dent. A. J. *29*:635-643, 1963.

Formicola, A. J. and R. E. Binder. Commonly encountered problems. Dent. Clin. N. Am. *16*:573-582, 1972.

Frazier, A. and L. K. Lisonbee. Adolescent concerns with physique. School Rev. *58*:397-405, 1950.

Fukaya, M. Changes of the patterns of pre- and post-operative behavior in mandibular protrusion, a psychological point of view: Three case reports. Jap. J. P. R. S. *21*:134-138, 1978.

Gabriel, H. F. Motivation of the headgear patient. Angle Orthodont. *38*(2), 129-135, 1968.

Gellert E., J. S. Girgus and J. Cohen. Children's awareness of their bodily appearance: a developmental study of factors associated with the body perception. Genet. Psychol. Monogr. *84*(1):109-174, 1971.

Giddon, D. B., L. E. Hershon and B. Lennartson. Discrepancy between objective and subjective profile measures. Scand. J. Dent. Res. *82*:527-535, 1974.

Goffman, E. *Stigma: Notes on the Management of Spoiled Identity*. Prentice Hall Inc., New Jersey, 1963.

Goin, M. K., R. W. Burgoyne and J. M. Goin. Face-lift operation: The patient's secret motivations and reactions to "informed consent". J. Plast. Reconstr. Surg. *59*:273-279, 1976.

Gold, S. L. Plaque-control motivation in orthodontic practice. Am. J. Orthodont. *68*:8-14, 1975.

Graber, T. M. The use of muscle forces by simple orthodontic appliances. Am. J. Orthodont. 76:1-20, 1979.

Hay, G. G. Psychiatric aspects of cosmetic nasal operations. Brit. J. Psychiatry 116(530):85-97, 1970.

Hilzenrath, S. S. and D. L. Baldwin. Achievement motivation - A factor in seeking orthodontic treatment. Dent. Res. 49:433, 1970.

Hilzenrath, S. S. and D. C. Baldwin. Relation between objective and subjective assessment of malocclusion. Int. Assoc. Dent. Res. (Abstr. #865), 1971.

Horowitz, H. S., L. K. Cohen and J. Doyle. Occlusal relations in children in an optimally fluoridated community. IV. Clinical and social psychological findings. Angle Orthodont. 41(3):189-201, 1971.

Howitt, J. W., G. Stricker and R. G. Eastman. Esthetic Index. New York State Dent. J.33:215, 1967.

Hutton, C. E. Patients' evaluation of surgically corrected prognathism; survey of patients. J. Oral Surg. 25:225-228, 1967.

Ingervall, B. and B. Hedeguard. Awareness of malocclusion and desire of orthodontic treatment in 18-year-old Swedish men. Acta. Odontol. Scand. 32(2):93-101, 1974.

Jacobson, A. Psychology and early orthodontic treatment. Am. J. Orthodont. 76:511-529, 1979.

Jensen, S. H. The psychological dimensions of oral and maxillofacial surgery: A critical review of the literature. J. Oral Surg. 36:447-453, 1978.

Jersild, A. T. The Psychology of Adolescence. The Macmillan Company, New York, 1968.

Joshi, S. and M. K. Prokash. The child in orthodontic practice. Int. J. Orthodont. 16:9-13, 1978.

Klima, R. J. Difference in perception of body image and self-concept between prospective orthodontic patients, their mothers, retention patients and a control group. Master's Thesis, Medical College of Virginia, 1975.

Klima, R. J., J. K. Wittemann and J. E. McIver. Body image, self-concept, and the orthodontic patient. Am. J. Orthodont. 75:507-516, 1979.

Knorr, N. J., M. T. Edgerton and J. E. Hoopes. The "insatiable" cosmetic surgery patient. J. Plast. Reconstr. Surg. 40:285-291, 1967.

Krajicek, D.D. Esthetic considerations prior to tooth removal. Dent. Clin. N. Am. 13(4):883-898, 1969a.

Krajicek, D. D. Guides for natural facial appearance as related to complete denture construction. J. Prosthet. Dent. 21(6):654-662, 1969b.

Kreit, L., C. Burstone and L. Delman. Patient cooperation in orthodontic treatment. J. Am. Col. Dent. 35:327-332, 1968.

Laufer, D., D. Glick and A. Sharon. Patient motivation and response to surgical correction of prognathism. Oral Surg. 41:309-313, 1976.

Lerner, R. M. and E. Gellert. Body build identification preference and aversion in children. Dev. Psych. 1(5):456-462, 1969.

Lerner, R. M. and S. J. Korn. The development of body build stereotypes in males. Child Dev. 43:912-920, 1972.

Lerner, R. M. and T. Moore. Sex and status effects on perception of physical attractiveness. Psychol. Rep. 34:1047-1050, 1974.

Lerner, R. M., J. B. Orlos and J. R. Knapp. Physical attractiveness, physical effectiveness and self-concept in late adolescence. Adolescence. *11*:313-326, 1976.

Lewit, D. W. and K. Virolainen. Conformity and independence in adolescents' motivation for orthodontic treatment. Child Dev. *39*:1189-1200, 1968.

Linn, E. L. Social meaning of dental appearance. J. Health and Hum. Behav. *1*:289-295, 1966.

MacGregor, F. C. Some psycho-social problems associated with facial deformities. Am. Sociol. Rev. *16*:629-638, 1951.

MacGregor, F. C. Social and cultural components in the motivations of persons seeking plastic surgery of the nose. J. Health Soc. Behav. *8*(2):125-135, 1967.

MacGregor, F. C. Social and psychological implications of dentofacial disfigurement. Angle Orthodont. *40*:231-238, 1970.

MacGregor, F. C., T. M. Abel, A. Bryt, E. Laver and S. Weissman. *Facial Deformities and Plastic Surgery: A Psychosocial Study*. C.C. Thomas, Springfield, Illinois, 1953.

Mahoney, E. R. and M. D. Finch. The dimensionality of body cathexis. J. Psychol. *92*:277-279, 1976.

Maj, G. A., G. Grilli and M. F. Belleti. Psychologic appraisal of children facing orthodontic treatment. Am. J. Orthodont. *53*:849-857, 1967.

McCandless, B. R. *Adolescents*. Dryden Press, Hinsdale, Illinois, 1970.

Meerloo, J. A. The fate of one's face. Psychiat. Quart. *30*:31-36, 1956.

Merrifield, J. M. The effects of orthodontic treatment on the physical characteristics pertaining to the attractiveness of the adolescent female. Master's Thesis. St. Louis University, 1976.

Meyer, E., W. E. Jacobson, M. T. Edgerton and A. Carter. Motivational patterns in patients seeking elective plastic surgery: Women who seek rhinoplasty. Psychosom. Med. *22*:193-198, 1960.

Meyer, J. K., J. E. Hoopes, M. E. Jabaley and R. Allen. Is plastic surgery effective in the rehabilitation of deformed delinquent adolescents? Plast. Reconstr. Surg. *51*:53-58, 1973.

Miller, E. S. and L. L. Larson. A theory of psycho-orthodontics with practical application to office techniques. Angle Orthodont. *49*:85-91, 1979.

Minihan, N. Relationships among self-perceived physical attractiveness, body shape, and personality of teenage girls. Ph.D. Dissertation. University of Illinois, Champaign, Illinois, 1971.

Mischel, W. Delay gratification, need for achievement and acquiescence in another culture. J. Abnorm. Soc. Psych. *62*:543-552, 1961.

Montague, J. B. and E. G. Epps. Attitudes toward social mobility as revealed by samples of Negro and white boys. Pac. Soc. Rev. *1*:81-84, 1958.

Moore, E. Patient motivation. Proc. Found. Orthodont. Res., pp. 99-107, 1972.

Murphy, D., Preorthodontic patient and his orthodontic treatment. Master's Thesis. University of Detroit, Detroit, Michigan, 1976.

Myrberg, N. and B. Thilander. An evaluation of the duration and the results of orthodontic treatment. Scand. J. Dent. Res. *81*:85-91, 1973.

Newman, G. V. Adult orthodontics. Dent. Surv. *54*:24-34, 1978.

Nicoletis, C. Morphology and psychology. Psychother. and Psychosomat. *21*:101-104, 1972.

Olley, P.C., Aspects of plastic surgery: Social and psychological sequelae. Brit. Med. J. *3*:322-324, 1974*a*.

Olley, P. C. Aspects of plastic surgery: psychiatric aspects of referral. Brit. Med J. *3*:248-249, 1974*b*.

Oullette, P. Psychological ramifications of facial change in relation to orthodontic treatment and orthognathic surgery. J. Oral Surg. *36*:787-790, 1978.

Oullette, P. The psychological impact of dramatic facial change. J. Clin. Orthodont. *13*:668-673, 1979.

Peterson, K. C. The importance of a single physical characteristic in the imputation of personality traits and the patterns of preference in the perceiver. Diss. Abstr. *36*(10-B):5275-5276, 1976.

Peterson, L. J. and R. G. Topazian. The pre-operative interview and psychological evaluation of the orthognathic surgery patient. J. Oral Surg. *32*:583-588, 1974.

Picard, C. F. Surgical correction of mandibular prognathism. Dent. Surg. *40*:35-39, 1964.

Pierce, M. H. A review of psychological aspects of malocclusion. S. Carolina Dent. J., pp. 15-17, 1971.

Piers, E. *Manual for the Piers-Harris Children's Self Concept Scale, Counselor Recordings and Tests*, Nashville, Tenn., 1969.

Pitt, E. J. and K. Korabik. The relationship between self-concept and profile self-perception. Am. J. Orthodont. *72*:459-460, 1977.

Reich, J. Factors influencing patient satisfaction with the results of esthetic plastic surgery. Plast. Reconstr. Surg. *55*:5-17, 1975.

Reiss, A. J., O. D. Duncan, P. K. Hatt and C. C. North. *Occupations and Social Status*. McMillan and Company, New York, 1962.

Reuss, A. L. A comparative study of cleft palate children and their siblings. J. Clin. Psychol. *21*:354-361, 1965.

Reuss, A. Convergent psychosocial factors in the cleft palate clinic. In: *Cleft Palate Habilitation*, R. M. Lancione (ed.), Syracuse Univerisity Press, Syracuse, New York, 1967.

Robinson, J. P. and P. R. Shaver. *Measures of Social Psychological Attitudes*. Institute for Social Research, University of Michigan, Ann Arbor, Michigan, 1973.

Root, W. R. Face value. Am. J. Orthodont. *35*:697-703, 1949.

Rosenberg, M. Malocclusion and craniofacial malformation: Self-concept implications. In: *Psychological Aspects of Craniofacial Malformations*, G. Stricker, E. Clifford, L. K. Cohen, D. B. Giddon and L. H. Meskin (eds.), N.I.D.R., Washington, D. C., 1975.

Rozner, L. Attitudes to cosmetic surgery. Med. J. Aust. *2*:513-516, 1973.

Rutzen, R. S. The social importance of orthodontic rehabilitation: Report of a five-year follow-up study. J. Health Soc. Behav. *14*:233-240, 1973.

Sarason, B. S., F. F. Davison, R. R. Naite and B. K. Ruebush. *Anxiety in Elementary School Children*. Wiley, New York, New York, 1960.

Schonbu, S. S. and R. E. Chell. Judgments of body appearance by fat and skinny male college students. Percept. Mot. Skills *24*(3):999-1002, 1967.

Schroeder, C. An evaluation of long-term benefits of dental treatment for dento-facial handicapped children in Colorado. J. Colo. Dent. Assoc. *50*(3):17-20, 1972.

Schwaninger, B. and N. Vickers-Schwaninger. Developing an effective oral hygiene program for the orthodontic patient: Review, rationale and recommendations. Am. J. Orthodont. *75*:447-452, 1979.

Schweckendiek, W. Psychological studies in patients with clefts. Cleft Palate J. *7*:533-539, 1970.

Secord, P. F. and C. W. Backman. Malocclusion and psychological factors. J. Am. Dent. Assoc. *59*:931-938, 1959.

Shaw, W. L., H. G. Lewis and N. R. Robertson. Perception of malocclusion. Brit. Dent. J. *138*:211-216, 1975.

Simmons, R. G. and F. Rosenberg. Sex, sex roles and self-image. J. Youth and Adolescence *4*:229-258, 1975.

Sims, M. Psychological disturbances associated with a mutilated malocclusion. J. Clin. Orthodont. *6*(6):341-345, 1972.

Spater, H. W., I. Fingeroth and M. M. Fingeroth. Psychological considerations of orthodontic treatment: A subjective study. Am. Dent. *30*:28-36, 1971.

Story, I. R. Psychological issues in orthodontic practice. Am. J. Orthodont. *52*(8):584-598, 1966.

Stricker, G. Psychological issues pertaining to malocclusion. Am. J. Orthodont. *58*(3):276-283, 1970.

Stricker, G. E., E. Clifford, L. K. Cohen, D. B. Giddon, L. H. Meskin and C. A. Evans. Psychological aspects of craniofacial disfigurement: A "State of the Art" assessment conducted by the Craniofacial Anomalies Program Branch, National Institute of Dental Research. Am. J. Orthodont. *76*:410-422, 1979.

Summers, C. J. The occlusal index: A system for identifying and scoring occlusal disorders. Am. J. Orthodont. *59*(6):552-567, 1971.

Sykes, B. E., T. A. Curtis and R. Caster. Psychosocial aspects of maxillofacial rehabilitation. Part II. A long-range evaluation. J. Prosthet. Dent. *28*(5):540-545, 1972.

Tisza, V. B. and E. Gumpertz. The parent's reaction to the birth and early care of children with cleft palate. Pediatrics, *30*:86-90, 1962.

Virolainen, K. Social and psychological factors in the adolescent attitudes toward orthodontic treatment. Master's Thesis. University of Michigan, Ann Arbor, Michigan, 1967.

Vojdani, A. and H. Horigan. The concept of orthodontic treatment for the adult. Acta Med. Iran *20*:129-136, 1977.

Walley, K. M. A survey of attitudes in respect to malocclusion and its treatment. Unpublished thesis. Am. Bd. Orthodont., St. Louis, Missouri, 1952.

Warford, J. H. An analysis of the factors motivating children to seek orthodontic treatment. Master's Thesis, Northwestern University, Chicago, Illinois, 1973.

Watson, C. G. Personality and adjustment in boys with cleft lips and palates. Cleft Palate J. *1*:130-138, 1964.

Weiss, J. Body image in orthodontics. J. New Jersey Dent. Assoc. *45*:14-17, 1973.

Weiss, J. and H. M. Eiser. Psychological timing of orthodontic treatment. Am. J. Orthodont. *72*:198-204, 1977.

Wiratmadja, R. M. Notes on esthetic surgery in the Indonesian. Clin. Plast. Surg. *1*(1):173-178, 1974.

Wirls, C. J. Psychological aspects of cleft lip and palate. In: *Cleft Lip and Palate.* W.C. Grabb, S. W. Rosenstein and K. R. Bzoch (eds.), Little, Brown and Company, Boston, 1971.

Woods, L. W. Psychiatry, body image and cosmetic surgery. Appl. Therap. *10*(7):451-454, 1968.

Zadok, A. B. The psychological reaction of children to orthodontic appliances (removable). Int. J. Orthodont. *3*(1):11-14, 1965.

PSYCHOLOGICAL EVALUATION OF FACIAL CHANGE FOLLOWING ORTHOGNATHIC SURGERY

Anne C. Redmond, M.D.

Assistant Professor of Psychiatry
University of Maryland and The Johns Hopkins Medical Institution

Lawrence Donner, Ph.D.

Associate Professor of Psychiatry
University of Maryland

Donald Tilghman, D.D.S.

Associate Professor and Director
Division of Dentistry and Oral and Maxillofacial Surgery
The Johns Hopkins Medical Institution

Physical attractiveness seems to be a most important asset in this culture. Much evidence has been accumulated which suggests that attractive people are perceived to possess almost every socially desirable character trait. In comparison to less attractive persons, the physically attractive are rated more sexually warm and responsive, sensitive, kind, interesting, strong, poised, modest, sociable and outgoing. They are perceived as living better lives than their unattractive peers (see Berscheid, '74, for a review). Moreover, there is some evidence that a person's impressions of an individual based on an assessment of physical attractiveness are communicated to that individual and influence his or her response behavior in the direction of the stereotype (Snyder *et al.*, '77). Thus, appearance seems to have a profound effect on social interaction and personality development.

Attractiveness seems to be largely determined by facial appearance. One can hide other unattractive body features with clothing; however, facial defects can only be masked in a limited fashion with make-up or hair style. Therefore, with the advent of dental and surgical techniques for facial reconstruction, many people who otherwise would have had to remain unattractive are seeking professional help to improve their appearance.

This paper will first review the literature regarding patients with facial defects who seek surgery and then concentrate on patients who elect orthognathic surgery. A typical patient will be described, a research project outlined, and three complex patients with psychological and dentofacial problems which necessitated psychiatric consultation will be discussed.

LITERATURE REVIEW

A review of the literature reveals that patients with facial defects who seek surgery can be classified into four categories: 1) those who seek correction of severe craniofacial deformities; 2) those who have suffered a traumatically induced deformity; 3) those who seek cosmetic surgery; and 4) those who have been referred for orthognathic surgery. Although there are overlapping physical and social features, there also seem to be differences.

Group I: Craniofacial Malformations

These patients quite often have severe congenital deformities, such as Cruzon's syndrome or hypertelorism. Parents have sought help for their child at birth or during early childhood, depending upon when the defect became observable. Many of these patients have had a series of operations during childhood (Murray, '73). MacGregor and co-workers' ('53) classic study of these patients revealed that the parent-family relationships were disrupted by the deformity. The parents' initial response of shock, anger, and shame was followed by grieving and only partial resolution. These families were stressed further by repeated surgeries, dwindling financial resources, societal response to the defect, and their overinvestment in the deformed child. However, MacGregor reported that more severely deformed patients seem to have a somewhat better psychological adjustment than less severely deformed patients. The worst deformities seemed to elicit consistent responses such as pity and revulsion from other people, whereas the lesser deformities elicited mixed and unpredictable responses which included much derision and humiliation. Furthermore, the earlier the surgical correction was initiated in childhood, the better was the person's emotional adjustment (MacGregor *et al.*, '53, MacGregor, '79).

As with most of these studies, however, the research design, which consisted of in-depth interviews and subjectively interpreted psychological tests, can be criticized because of its subjectivity. One might wonder if the patients who have severe craniofacial deformities, obtain surgery early and have some psychosocial family intervention have a better or worse psychological adjustment than the patients who undergo orthognathic surgery for less severe deformities. A long term objective study of children in both categories using matched, facially average children as controls would be a welcome addition to the literature.

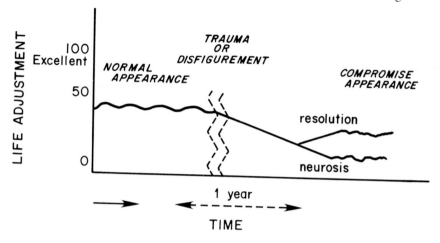

Figure 1. Factors which increase the likelihood of patients being satisfied with their surgical procedures.

Group II: Trauma Patients

The second group consists of patients who have a normal appearance until experiencing sudden trauma, either accidental or surgical. These patients initially exhibit symptoms of acute situational stress. Illness or injury has created facial disfigurement which causes a sudden life change. As with any severe crisis, the individual grieves. He must reconcile his perception of society's idealized facial image and his previous internalized facial image with his feelings when seeing his now damaged face in the mirror. He must also work through his reactions to other peoples' new responses when viewing his face. The more idealized is his image, the more difficult is the adjustment (Reiner, '72). Resolution involves either coming to terms with facial changes or having an increase in psychiatric symptoms and social disability (Fig. 1). The literature indicates that many of these people socially withdraw after disfigurement (MacGregor et al., '53; Molinaro, '78). Traumatic deformities acquired in childhood, especially in infancy or early adolescence, seem to create more psychosocial problems than those acquired in adulthood. Adults have had the experience of being accepted as normal for many years before the trauma, and so they usually have a better life adjustment following the injury. They may also have more coping mechanisms available than do younger patients (Murray, '73). Adult patients, on the other hand, may be more dissatisfied with the surgical results than the younger patients, their fantasy being that the surgeon should be able to return their appearance to its previous condition. However, the nature of many injuries does not permit this (Bryt, '66b).

Group III: Elective Plastic Surgery

The third group consists of patients who request cosmetic surgery. The descriptive literature cites numerous examples of psychopathology found among patients in this group which make them prime targets for dissatisfaction with surgical results (Hill and Silver, '66; Bryt, '66a, '66b; Knorr et al., '67). Elective surgery patients at psychological risk fall into three categories. The first is composed of those patients who use their facial deformity as an explanation for all of their negative life experiences. Removing the deformity may strip them of a crucial defense, thus precipitating other, perhaps more severe, psychiatric problems, such as depression and/or intense anger at the surgeon (Hill and Silver, '66; Bryt, '66a, '66b). The second category consists of those patients who, experiencing external life stress, such as a relationship that is dissolving or increasing job difficulty, seek plastic surgery in the hopes that a more attractive face will prevent the unwanted outcome. Since appearance is usually only a small part of the difficulty, surgery usually does *not* lead to the desired outcome (Knorr et al., '67). The third group is made up of psychotic individuals who have somatic delusions about their appearance. Frequently, the surgeon is also incorporated into the delusional system. The facial defects are usually minimal, but these patients describe them in a bizarre fashion. Surgery does not treat the basic psychotic illness, so little improvement ensues (Knorr et al., '67)

Patients who do not fall into these high risk categories tend to be the best candidates for corrective surgery. Even though they may have substantial psychological problems, they seem to benefit from a change in self-esteem following plastic surgery. It is even more likely that these patients will be satisfied with the results of surgery if 1) the patient has been carefully evaluating the advantages and disadvantages of surgery *for a number of months* after initial consultation, before the actual operation takes place; 2) the patient can concretely explain what is wrong and what he/she expects the outcome of the surgery to be; 3) when given an explanation of the surgical procedure and its expected results, the patient can repeat this with little distortion; 4) he/she can explain the surgical risks as well as the benefits; 5) perhaps most importantly, the patient is choosing surgery primarily for his/her own benefit and not because others want him or her to have the procedure; and, finally, 6) the patient does *not* convey a sense of desperation (Edgerton and Knorr, '71; Olley, '74; Table 1).

Objective studies of plastic surgery patients are few and the percentages of severely emotionally disturbed applicants ranged from 0 to 16% (Edgerton et al., '60; Hay '70; Olley, '74; Reich, '75; LeJour and LeCocq, '75). LeJour and Le Cocq ('75) examined 68 patients who underwent cosmetic surgery. Fifty-seven percent were "adapted", 31% "worried",

Table 1. Promoting Satisfaction

1. Time between initial consultation and surgery is several months
2. Surgeon and patient meet several times before surgery
3. Patient request is realistic
4. Surgeon promises realistic results
5. Surgeon explains benefits vs. risks
6. Patient demonstrates clear understanding of 3 and 4
7. Patient wants surgery for himself
8. Patient is not desperate

and 12% "distressed". Of the 62 patients evaluated post-operatively, 13% were dissatisfied with the results. All but one had been classified "worried" or "distressed" prior to surgery.

Reich's ('75) studies are the most extensive. He studied 750 patients in 1967 and 900 patients in 1973. In the 1967 study, 62% of the patients were judged to be either emotionally unstable or unduly concerned about their appearance; 36% were judged to be emotionally normal. In the 1973 study, 68% of the patients were judged to be normal emotionally, and 30% were judged to be emotionally unstable or unduly concerned about their appearance. Despite this apparent shift in psychopathology, 30% of the patients in both studies were dissatisfied with the results at the end of three months; 8% were dissatisfied for esthetic reasons and 22% because they had not obtained relief from psychosocial problems. Follow-up studies done between one and four years post-surgery revealed a dissatisfaction rate of 15%; 5% were dissatisfied for esthetic reason and 10% due to psychosocial problems. All dissatisfied patients reported that one or more close family members and friends had responded negatively to the surgery. Reich ('75) also evaluated 100 consecutive rhinoplasty patients. Three months after surgery, twenty-four of the patients were dissatisfied. Eighteen of these were reassessed one year later. Seven of these were now satisfied, and eleven still were not. Only four of the eleven related their dissatisfaction to a visible nasal deformity. The others were unhappy with the esthetic or psychosocial result.

Hay's ('70) preoperative study was an attempt to gather objective psychological data on surgery patients. Forty-five patients were evaluated prior to rhinoplasty, using standard psychological tests and interviews. The patients and independent raters evaluated photographs of their facial deformities, rating them on a scale from one (perfect features) to nine (very marked imperfections). Matched controls were identically evaluated. Results indicated that the patient group was significantly more obsessive, introverted and intropunitive than the control group. They also scored higher on neuroticism, personal illness, and general hostility. The psychological testing data was about the same for patients with mild deformities as for those with marked deformities. There was some indication from the psychiatric interviews that the least severely deformed had more psychopathology; however, the author dismissed this as possible researcher bias and chose to use his objective data to view the patients as a homogenous group—more disturbed than the general population.

Hay and Heather ('73) compared the preoperative and postoperative psychological testing data of seventeen rhinoplasty patients. The results showed that, as a group, there was significant reduction of personal illness and general hostility following surgery. Patients' attitudes became more extrapunitive, and their personality traits became more hysteroid. They concluded that patients with minimal disfigurement do as well following surgery as those with severe disfigurement.

Group IV: Dento-facial Malformation

These patients have been referred for evaluation of combined orthodontic and maxillofacial surgical treatment. In contrast to patients who have severe craniofacial deformities, this group of patients usually has more subtle abnormalities but represents a larger portion of the general population. The literature regarding this kind of patient consists of a few studies in which questionnaires were answered by patients (Hutton, '67; Wictorin *et al.*, '69; Crowell *et al.*, '70; Hillerstrom *et al.*, '71; Wilcox, '72; Laufer *et al.*, '76; Ouellette, '78) and several descriptive or review articles (Peterson and Topazian, '76; Jensen, '78; Peterson and Topazian, '76; Stricker *et al.*, '79). Psychosocial profiles of these patients are not available in the literature. Peterson and Topazian ('76) had to rely on the plastic surgery literature to develop their preoperative questionnaire, which was designed to screen for potentially dissatisfied patients. However, are the patients with dentofacial malformations who are anticipating orthognathic surgery really similar to the plastic surgery patients who anticipate that soft tissue surgical procedures will produce an improvement in appearance?

One difference does emerge immediately in reviewing the literature; unlike the cosmetic surgery patient who is generally self-referred, between 55% and 94% of the patients in these studies were referred by orthodontists, general dentists or physicians. As noted by Jensen ('78), there may be a psychological difference between self-referred and other-referred patients. At the very least, other-referral means there is an increase in the time between defining the problem and seeking the solution.

A second difference is that although the predominant reason for seeking treatment in both groups is esthetics, a substantial proportion of orthognathic surgery patients indicate that functional concerns are first or second reasons for seeking surgery. In one study, 32% of the patient

Table 2. Dissatisfaction with Orthognathic Surgery

Study	N	Dissatisfied
Hutton (1967)	32	3%
Crowel et al. (1970)	49	4%
Hillerstrom et al. (1971)	33	3%
Laufer (1976)	28	4%
Oullette (1978)	66	7%

sample cited difficulty in chewing as the primary reason for seeking treatment (Laufer et al., '76) as did 74 of 95 patients (78%) in another study (Wictorin et al., '69).

A third difference is that orthognathic surgery patients must undergo extensive evaluation after which they commit themselves to reasonably long-term orthodontic treatment. In some cases, periodontic treatment prior to surgery is also needed. This commitment to a potentially traumatic and cosmetically unattractive long-term treatment plan requires very high patient motivation. One can preoperatively evaluate motivation and compliance to treatment by observing the day-to-day status of the patient's oral hygiene and his cooperation in the first phase of orthodontic treatment. The plastic surgeon does not have this luxury when dealing with soft tissue surgical changes, most of which do not require extensive patient preparation.

There is a fourth difference—that seen in patient dissatisfaction rates. Orthognathic surgery patients seem to be less dissatisfied with the results of surgery. This may be the result of differences in timing of treatment and in motivation mentioned above or the result of differences in variables not yet explored. The highest dissatisfaction rate for orthognathic patients was 7% (n=66) found by Ouellette ('78; Table 2). This is less than the 15% dissatisfaction rate reported for cosmetic surgery patients by Reich ('75) or the 13% reported by LeJour and LeCocq ('75).

Nevertheless, there are similarities between elective plastic surgery and orthognathic surgery patients. A substantial number of both types of patients report reduced self-consciousness, increased self-esteem and improved social relations following surgery. Twenty-three percent of Ouellette's ('78) patients reported an extreme life change, and 37% reported a moderate life change following treatment. However, since some of these patients had only orthodontic treatment the implications for surgery are unclear. More importantly, all of these studies have relied on patient reporting and anecdotal material gathered at varying time periods and, therefore, can only serve as a stimulus for future, more methodologically sound and empirically based psychosocial research (Jensen, '78).

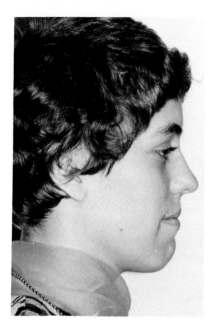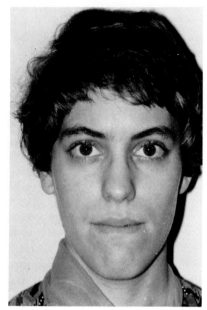

Figure 2. Pretreatment facial views of patient R. Note the excessive lower facial height, a slight deficiency in both intraorbital rim areas, slight narrowing of the ala bases, mentalis muscle strain on closing of the lips and a slightly contour-altered chin.

A TYPICAL CLINICAL CASE

Clinical History

A typical patient history of a satisfied orthognathic patient is that of thirty year-old patient, R. The patient was referred by her general dentist for an orthognathic surgery workup (Fig. 2). She had excessive lower facial height, a slight deficiency in both infraorbital rim areas, a slight narrowing of the ala bases, excessive display of the upper incisor teeth below the upper lip, excessive interlabial gap with lip incompetence, gingival exposure upon smiling, mentalis muscle strain on closing of the lips, and a slightly contour-altered chin. Intra-oral examination revealed a bilateral crossbite, a tendency toward an openbite, labially positioned maxillary canines, V-shaped anterior maxillary arch, and missing lower right and left first molars (Fig. 3).

Cephalometric evaluation substantiated the presence of an excessive lower facial height, an anterior open bite and a steep mandibular plane (Fig. 4). She was diagnosed as having vertical facial excess, an anterior and buccal segment crossbite, and a contour-deficient chin.

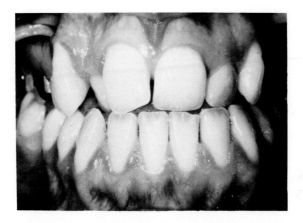

Figure 3. Pretreatment intraoral view of patient R. Note the bilateral cross-bite, a tendency toward open-bite, labially positioned maxillary canines, a V-shaped anterior maxillary arch and missing lower right and left first molars.

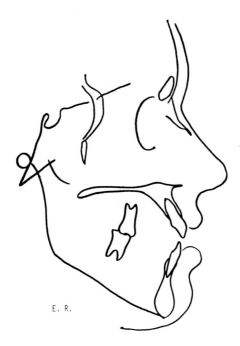

E. R.

Figure 4. The pretreatment lateral cephalometric tracing of patient R reveals an excessive lower facial height, an anterior open bite and a steep mandibular plane.

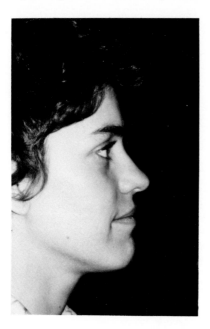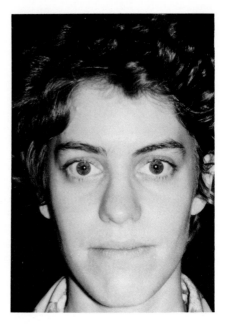

Figure 5. Post-treatment facial views of patient R demonstrating improvement in facial height, profile, infraorbital regions, ala base areas, mentalis muscle strain and chin.

Treatment objectives included reducing the lower facial vertical excess, increasing the infraorbital prominence, widening the ala bases, reducing the exposure of the maxillary incisor teeth, reducing the interlabial lip gap, correcting the excessive gingival smile, improving mentalis muscle function and improving the chin contour.

Treatment consisted of performing a maxillary, superior repositioning-advancement Le Fort I osteotomy with a left buccal segment lateral/ anterior osteotomy to close the edentulous space and to correct the cross-bite. The anterior aspect of the maxilla was intruded 7 mm posteriorly and advanced 3 mm anteriorly. A bone graft from the mandible was used to stabilize the left buccal segment. The mandible was autorotated creating a 5 mm advancement at pogonion and a 7 mm superior repositioning at menton. The results are evident when comparing the preoperative data (Figs. 2, 3, and 4) with the postoperative data (Figs. 5, 6 and 7). Note how her appearance has changed from that of being minimally cosmetically unattractive to that of being attractive.

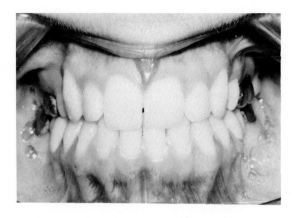

Figure 6. The post-treatment intraoral view of patient R showing correction of dental deformities.

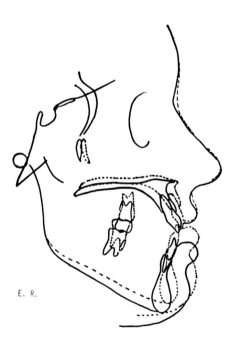

E. R.

Figure 7. The pre- and post-treatment superimposed lateral cephalometric tracings of patient R. The pretreatment tracing is depicted by the solid lines and the post-treatment tracing by the broken lines.

129

Personal History

R grew up on a farm in a rural section of an eastern state. Her father owned a small business which failed during R's adolescence. He experienced a subsequent decline in his career and currently has a medical disability. R remembers him as warm and affectionate but deeply depressed by his lack of success; she was his favorite child. Her older brother was her mother's favorite.

R's mother worked part-time until R was twelve and full-time as a nurse thereafter. A domineering woman, she and R frequently clashed until she returned to work full-time and R began to cook and clean house, after which the two drew closer. R currently has much affection and concern for both parents.

R remembers being isolated throughout her childhood and being teased about her face in school. She was an excellent student and was praised by her parents and her teachers for her achievement. She was a tomboy until age eleven, when she began to wish she appeared more attractive. At age thirteen, her mother would frequently examine her mouth, saying, "You are becoming ugly." R did not date during her adolescence. She remembers a painful incident when a boy—seeing her for the first time—told her she was ugly.

Upon entering college, R was exposed to the idea of surgery for the first time. She had had no dental care in her childhood, having been led to believe she would be more attractive with false teeth which would be acquired in adulthood. Both her father and mother had worn false teeth since middle adulthood. According to her family, her father's appearance had improved, and she believed that the same would happen to her.

R was referred to an oral surgeon at age eighteen after several abcessed teeth were extracted by a general dentist. Distrustful of the surgeon, she refused treatment, a decision encouraged by her mother.

During college, R dated one man seriously but chose to go to graduate school instead of getting married. She calls herself an overachiever. In graduate school she dated rarely, although she had platonic men friends. Her dentist during this time referred her to an orthodontist, who subsequently referred her to the oral and maxillofacial surgery clinic for evaluation for a coordinated treatment of surgery and orthodontics. This time she chose the surgery because she was impressed with the surgeon's competence.

R had an uneventful preoperative, operative and postoperative course, with the exception of needing a polyp removed from her vocal chords six weeks after surgery. She is very satisfied with her surgical results and believes that she has received excellent care from her surgeons. During the two and one-half years after surgery she has experienced substantial personality changes. She reports having more self-confidence, liking herself more, being sought after by men at parties, being told often that she is pretty, and having men tell her she appears younger than she is. She has learned to dance and is enjoying her social life; however, she is concerned about her diminishing interest in her career at a time when she is working on her doctoral thesis. She feels that she is experiencing the adolescence she never had. The changes have been so positive that she was willing to give us consent for this presentation.

RESEARCH DESIGN

Given our interest in the changes which such patients as R seem to undergo and the lack of any standardized psychological data in the literature, the following research design is currently being implemented by the authors in hopes of adding to our knowledge.

Subjects

The subjects consist of 100 consecutive private patients electing major maxillary and mandibular surgery who consented to participate in this research project during their treatment. The subjects serve as their own controls, in addition to which there is a control group consisting of 100 matched (on age, sex, race and education) patients seeking traditional orthodontic dental care

Assessment Procedure

All subjects who participate are evaluated using a series of psychological assessment procedures, including objective tests and attitudinal rating scales. The assessment procedure, which begins with initial contact for treatment, is divided into three parts: pretreatment (Pre), post-treatment (Post) and Follow-up. All assessments on visits prior to surgery will be designated Pre. All assessments occurring within the first month following surgery are designated Post, all assessments occurring one month or more after surgery are designated Follow-up.

Each patient is given the following tests: 1) Multiple Affect Adjective Check List (MAACL; Zuckerman, '60); 2) Minnesota Multiphasic Personality Inventory (MMPI; Hathaway and McKinley, '51); 3) Mooney Problem Check List (MPCL; Gordon and Mooney, '50); and 4) the Semantic Differential (SD; Osgood *et al.*, '57). In addition, every fourth patient is given a standard psychiatric interview. Table 3 illustrates the assessment techniques specifying the visit on which each test/interview is administered and the estimated total time in minutes the assessment takes.

Table 3.

Assessment Technique	Pretreatment Visits					Post-treatment Visits		Follow-up Visits						Number of Visits/Patient			
	1	2	3	4	5 Surgery	6	7	8	9	10	11	12	13	Pre	Post	Follow up	Total
							One	Three Months	Six Months	One	Two	Five Years	Ten				
MAACL	X	X	X	X	X	X	X	X	X	X	X	X	X	5	2	6	13
MPCL & MMPI		X					X		X	X	X	X	X	1	1	5	7
Interview			X*				X*		X*	X*	X*	X*	X*	1	1	5	7*
SD			X				X	X	X	X	X	X	X	1	1	6	8
Total Estimated Time (Minutes)	5	105	50*	5	5	5	120*	35	120*	120*	120*	120*	120*	170	125	635	930

*Every 4th patient add 35 minutes

Each of the assessment techniques was specifically chosen to provide standardized and objective information on: 1) affect, 2) personality traits and characteristics, 3) problems in living, and 4) face and body concept attitudes.

Affect: MAACL. The MAACL is designed to measure three affects: anxiety, depression and hostility. The check list is well suited for this research in that it reflects daily changes in anxiety, anger and depression, and it can be rapidly completed and scored. The check list contains 132 adjectives. The anxiety scale consists of eleven adjectives which, when checked, are given one point each and ten adjectives which, when *not* checked, are also given one point each. Anxiety scores range from 0 to 21. On the depression scale, there are 20 adjectives which when checked are given 1 point each. Twenty adjectives which when *not* checked are also scored 1 point each. Depression scores range from 0 to 40. On the hostility scale there are 16 adjectives which are given one point each when checked and twelve adjectives which are given one point each when *not* checked. Hostility scores range from 0 to 28. The MAACL takes approximately five minutes to complete and is administered on every visit and immediately before surgery. This instrument will provide a measure of the subjects' changing affect states during Pre, Post and Follow-up.

Personality Traits and Characteristics: MMPI. The MMPI in its booklet version is a 566 true-false self-report inventory which is concerned with the assessment of personality and takes approximately sixty to seventy-five minutes to complete. The content of items is quite diverse. Raw scores are converted to standard scores on a profile sheet for interpretation (see Colligan *et al.*, in this volume). The MMPI profile sheet provides the clinician with information about the subject on four validity scales and ten clinical scales. The validity scales provide information about the reliability and validity of the clinical results. The clinical scales provide information about how the patient compares with people in the general population and with specific patient groups. An empirically derived questionnaire, the MMPI, is considered the *sin qua non* of psychometric tests. The MMPI is administered once during the pre- and postoperative periods and five times during the follow-up period (Table 3).

Problems in Living: MPCL (Adult Form). The MPCL is a self-administered, 288 statement—a list of problems that older teenagers and adults may have—written in simple and readily understood language. The areas covered include health, economic security, self-improvement, personality, home and family, courtship, sex, religion, and occupation. The subjects are asked to first go through the list of statements and

Table 4. Face and Body Concepts

1. My Face	10. My Cheek Bones
2. My Neck	11. My Nose
3. My Mouth	12. My Eyes
4. My Upper Teeth	13. My Eyebrows
5. My Lower Teeth	14. My Ears
6. My Upper Lip	15. My Forehead
7. My Lower Lip	16. My Hair
8. My Jaw	17. My Whole Body
9. My Chin	

underline those problems with which they are concerned. The subjects are then asked to look back over the problems they have underlined and to circle the numbers in front of those problems that are of the most concern to them. The MPCL is given pre- and postoperatively once and five times during the follow-up period. It takes about thirty minutes to complete and provides a standard measure of change in frequency or pattern of problems before and after surgical intervention.

Face and Body Concept: SD. This provides a measure of meaning for one or more concepts. It assesses the spatial distance between two or more concepts as well as between the same concepts rated on different occasions. Eleven scales with high factor loadings on the evaluation (E), potency (P) or activity (A) dimensions in Osgood's original factor analysis were chosen. Examples of scales with high loadings on E are *Ugly-Beautiful* and *Worthless-Valuable*; on P are *Strong-Weak* and *Hard-Soft*; and on A are *Excitable-Calm*. Three total scores—one for E, P and A for *each* of the seventeen concepts listed in Table 4—will be obtained by summing scale scores, which range from one to seven.

The SD is administered once during the pre- and postoperative periods and six times during the follow-up period, and focuses on whether or not there are any changes in face and body concept, and if there are any changes, it shows where and when those changes occur.

Some of the research questions we hope to address are the following:

Is there any correlation between psychological profile, satisfaction with surgery and postoperative complications?

Can patients at high psychological risk be determined by psychological testing?

What are some quantitative parameters of patients' psychosocial adjustment prior to and following surgery?

Is there a difference in the psychological personality profile and life adjustment between people with mild cosmetic deformities and those with more severe cosmetic deformities? Do these two groups respond differently after surgery?

Are there psychosocial problems which are more prevalent among facially deformed patients than nonfacially deformed patients?

Do people with different facial deformities have different psychological profiles or problems?

What happens to affect at the preoperative, operative, and postoperative stages?

What is intrapsychic facial imagery like before surgery? How does it shift after surgery?

Do orthognathic patients differ psychologically from orthodontic patients?

What psychological differences are found between adolescent patients and adult patients?

CASE STUDIES OF PATIENTS AT PSYCHOLOGICAL RISK

In the clinical practice of orthognathic surgery, situations arise which warrant a psychiatric or psychological consultation. Many situations are similar to those reported in the cosmetic surgery literature. Three patients from the pilot study just described whose cases illustrate the potential for postoperative dissatisfaction will be presented. These patients tend to fall in Peterson and Topazian's ('76) categories of neutral or negative reactors.

Hidden Motivation for Surgery

Clinical Evaluation. Patient L is an example of a person seeking surgery for a malocclusion which could either be corrected by orthodontic treatment alone or by a combination of orthodontic and orthognathic surgery. L complained about protrusive maxillary teeth. Clinical evaluation revealed that L had an acceptable full face and profile except for maxillary incisor/upper lip protrusion. Intra-oral examination revealed that L had a Class II, Division I malocclusion with some mild rotations, a moderate curve of Spee, no crowding in the lower arch and very minimal crowding in the upper arch. A treatment plan was proposed which included two alternatives, each involving the extraction of the first bicuspid teeth in the upper arch. The first choice was one of conventional orthodontics, with full upper and lower arch banded appliances, and involved a two-year plus treatment interval. The second choice was for L to wear full-banded appliances in both arches for approximately one year and then to have an anterior maxillary ostectomy with intra-arch fixation for six weeks.

Personal History and Psychological Evaluation. L is a thirty-year-old woman who has been embarrassed about her protruding teeth since childhood. She blamed herself for her protrusion because she sucked her thumb until adolescence. She wants her teeth to be straight for her own inner happiness. Three of her siblings had worn braces in adulthood, and she understands adult orthodontics. She is able to define her deformity and explain the surgical procedure. Thus far, L seems like a good candidate; but why does she seek surgery rather than orthodontics alone, except for the time factor? The explanation may lie in her imagined expectations from surgery. She believes that surgery will give her a more perfect result than orthodontics. She strives for perfection in all aspects of her life and frequently ends up feeling disappointed.

An examination of L's childhood further illuminates her quest for perfection and this request for surgery. She was the fourth of seven children born to upper middle class parents, both of whom were alcoholics. None of the children received orthodontic treatment at the age when their peers in private school were in braces. L was called "bucky beaver" by both family and peers, which made her furious and caused her to feel intense shame. Her parents separated when L was ten. She felt guilty because she had wished her father were dead, and she neglected a younger sister who was showing obvious signs of psychological maladjustment. L withdrew into herself, becoming an overachiever in school. After dating a modest amount in high school and college, she married for two years in her mid-twenties, but then divorced.

L currently owns her own home and supports a boyfriend who is not working. He is critical of her desire to correct her malocclusion by either method. Her mother died three years ago from alcoholism. Her father has joined Alcoholics Anonymous and begun to attempt reconciliation with her shortly before she sought surgical evaluation.

The surgery appears to be a way of punishing herself for her childhood anger and guilt, reawakened by her father's attempts at reconciliation. Her fantasy that "if my parents' mouths were wired, they could have stopped drinking" demonstrates her wish that this surgery, which requires intermaxillary fixation, could save her from her internal rage at and longing for her parents. Also, she believes she will feel less depressed if her teeth are more perfect.

Tests of L's mental status showed an obsessive personality style with moderate anxiety. Fortunately, she is currently in psychotherapy and was amenable to some tentative interpretations about her situation. She has begun to see that the surgical results might not serve to alleviate her anger and guilt about her parents and boyfriend. She is still considering the two modalities of corrective treatment for her protruding teeth.

High Risk for Panic in the Operative Phase

Clinical Evaluation. Twenty-two-year-old patient D is an example of a patient who has had extensive illness and hospitalization in childhood, leaving him with severe medical complications. He has had an iliostomy and currently has only one kidney. Evaluation revealed the patient to have a severe deformity with respect to the relationship of the maxilla to the mandible. He has a severely hypoplastic maxilla, an open bite from first molar to first molar with an inter-incisal space of 13 mm and a severe reverse curve of Spee in the lower arch. The mandible is rotated downward and backward with a severe obtuse gonial angle, short ramus and long corpus, and a steep mandibular plane. In addition, there is a severe lingual inclination of the lower incisor teeth and an 11 mm reverse overjet. His facies appear to be hypoplastic in the midface region, and there is excessive vertical and sagittal chin prominence in the lower face. The patient was presented with a detailed and involved surgical treatment plan outlining a LeFort I maxillary advancement osteotomy, double procedures in the mandible utilizing a bilateral wedge-shaped body ostectomy and a bilateral ramus procedure. Treatment included wearing fullbanded active orthodontic appliances for nine to twelve months.

Personal History and Psychological Evaluation. Psychiatric consultation was requested to evaluate whether or not D would be a good surgical risk. He was first referred by his dentist when he was seventeen but did not choose to come to the orthognathic surgery clinic until his supervisors at work forced him to shave his beard; the clean-shaven face accentuated his physical defect.

D is employed as a housekeeper at a local hotel and lives at home with his mother. He has some male friends, but has had no serious girlfriends. He has several hobbies, such as refinishing antique furniture.

D remembers being a friendly and outgoing child. He does not resemble anyone in his family but feels he takes after his mother. His parents separated when he was seven, and his father died when D was sixteen. He got along with his teachers and made average grades. Between the ages of eleven and fourteen he was hospitalized several times for a nephrectomy and an iliostomy. He remained home for two years during the seventh and eighth grades, requiring a home teacher. He remembers almost dying during this period. He has stated, "although kids would say 'where did you get that face?', I let it roll off me. I could be dead." When he returned to high school he felt awkward and different from his peers. He grew a beard as soon as he was able to, maintaining it until his supervisor forced him to shave.

D is afraid of being in a hospital again. He fears dying early, like his father, or damaging his good kidney. His mental status exam revealed a pleasant, coherent person of normal affect. Psychiatric assessment indicated that he is a good surgical risk if there are no medical contraindications to surgery. He understands the extent of his problem. He would like to improve his appearance and speak more clearly; it is his own idea to pursue surgery. However, it is possible that he will experience severe anxiety immediately preoperatively or postoperatively as he is flooded with affect and memories from his past hospitalizations and his father's death. Being in the recovery room may particularly stimulate recall of the panic of nearly dying. Some prophylactic counseling prior to surgery may be helpful, and he should receive counseling while in the hospital.*

Negative Response to Surgical Treatment

Clinical History. Patient C is an example of the dissatisfied postoperative patient. She is the only patient that the psychiatric consultant has been asked to evaluate in two years who is unhappy and seeking additional surgery. She stated "I am 50% better because my basic appearance is improved, but I am 50% worse because I don't look like I am smiling and I have a pucker in my chin." Not only does she want the corners of her mouth to turn up and the chin pucker removed, but she is also seeking a derma-abrasion. Two plastic surgeons with whom she has consulted are reluctant to operate because she has had two augmentation mammoplasties in past years which have displeased her. She is a 40-year-old, divorced, professional woman with chaotic present and past histories.

The patient was referred for orthognathic surgery consideration by a plastic surgeon with whom she had sought a consultation for derma-abrasions and a face lift. It was apparent from the onset that she was concerned with esthetics and not function. On initial examination she showed mild vertical facial excess, an extremely short upper lip, a severely gummy smile, and total exposure of the maxillary incisor teeth with the lips in repose. There was a Class II, Division I cusp-to-cusp malocclusion, and the patient had a contour-deficient chin on the saggital plane.

The treatment consisted of a maxillary LeFort I advancement osteotomy to correct the slight A-P discrepancy and to allow for autorotation of the mandible which would increase the chin prominence. The maxilla was also intruded 11 mm in an attempt to improve her severe interlabial lip gap and partially correct her gummy smile (she had been told that it would be impossible to totally correct it).

---

*D successfully tolerated surgery and is delighted with his results. The psychiatric consultant interviewed him two days before the procedures. His fears were discussed at that time and he did not subsequently experience panic. He was a model patient.

The treatment corrected her Class II malocclusion, giving her a stable, well interdigital Class I relationship with a good overbite and overjet. Eighty percent of the lip incompetence also was corrected by the surgical procedure. While she still shows excessive maxillary incisor teeth when the lips are in repose, there has been a dramatic improvement, and there is now a less gummy smile.

Her dissatisfaction lies in the resulting inferior repositioning of the commissures of the lips to the level of the buccal cervical margin of the crowns of the mandibular teeth and an increased fullness of the soft tissues in the midface cheek region as a result of some overshortening of the facial height in the attempt to correct the short upper lip. She feels there is now a reverse curve in her smile pattern and that her lower teeth are more visible than she would like. Two and one-half years after treatment she is still unhappy with this aspect of her result.

Personal History and Psychological Evaluation. C is currently experiencing serious job difficulty, and she is threatening to sue her employer for discrimination. She is not currently working in her area of specialization. She had been attending classes at a professional school but suddenly dropped her courses. She describes serious financial difficulties and is concerned about paying her mortgage. Her son has recently left home for college. She states that her main goal in life is to find a man, and she has been in a series of short-term, tempestuous relationships.

C's childhood was impoverished. Both parents worked while C did the cooking and cleaning. She was frequently ill with ear, nose and throat difficulties from infancy until age eight. At school, boys teased her brutally about her appearance, and she was a behavior problem during adolescence.

C suffered a severe depression after being deserted by a man who told her she was awful during a weekend outing with a group of people. She went into psychotherapy three different times as an adult, but always terminated treatment prematurely. She has a son from an affair with a substantially older man. Her mother helped her raise the child while she went to college and graduate school. She was married briefly in her mid-thirties to a man who had been previously divorced four times.

C's mental status exam revealed a labile affect, paranoid ideation, autistic tangential thinking, and many borderline psychotic features. For example, she initially thought the psychiatric consultant was a plastic surgeon, although she had been properly prepared to see a psychiatrist. Especially important to the dynamics of this patient is that she now resembles her mother, with whom she has a very ambivalent relationship. C has severe psychopathology and has been diagnosed as borderline personality disorder. She is a poor surgical candidate.

139

C has not been happy with either her mammoplasties or her orthognathic surgery. She can give no reason for wanting surgical revision other than, "I used to look like I smiled all the time, now I frown." She feels driven to obtain further surgery, believing it will help her find another intimate relationship. The surgery team, including the psychiatric consultant, has met with her three different times in order to elicit her precise concerns and to give her detailed accounts of the limitations of future surgery. She continues to communicate in a vague, distorted way. We are letting time pass to see how she adjusts and are maintaining contact with her.

REFERENCES

Berscheid, E. and E. Walster. Physical attractiveness. In: *Advances in Experimental Social Psychology*, Vol. 7, L. Berkowitz (ed.), Academic Press, New York, 1974.

Bryt, A. Psychiatric considerations in candidates for plastic surgery. Eye, Ear, Nose and Throat Monthly *45*:86-88, 1966*a*.

Bryt, A. Psychiatric considerations in candidates for plastic surgery. Eye, Ear, Nose and Throat Monthly *45*:102-105, 1966*b*.

Crowell, N. T., H. J. Sazima and S. T. Elder. Survey of patients' attitudes after surgical correction of prognathism: study of 33 patients. J. Oral Surg. *28*:818-822, 1970.

Edgerton, M. T., W. E. Jacobson and E. Meyer. Surgical-psychiatric study of patients seeking plastic (cosmetic) surgery: ninety-eight consecutive patients with minimal deformity. Brit. J. Plast. Surg. *13*:136, 1960.

Edgerton, M. T. and N. J. Knorr. Motivational patterns of patients seeking cosmetic (esthetic) surgery. Plast. & Reconstr. Surg. *48*(6):551-557, 1971.

Gordon and Mooney. Mooney Problem Check List, Adult Form and Manual. New York: The Psychological Corporation, 1950.

Hathaway, S. R. and J. C. McKinley. Minnesota Multiphasic Personality Inventory Manual. New York: Psychological Corporation, 1951.

Hay, G. G. Psychiatric aspects of cosmetic nasal operations. Brit. J. Psych. *116*:85-97, 1970.

Hay, G. and B. Heather. Changes in psychometric test results following cosmetic nasal operations. Brit. J. Psych. *122*:89-90, 1973.

Hill, G. and A. G. Silver. Psychodynamic and esthetic motivations for plastic surgery. Psychosom. Med. *12*:345-355, 1950.

Hillerstrom, K., S. Sorensen and L. Wictorin. Biological and psychosocial factors in patients with malformation of the jaws. Scand. J. Plast. Reconstr. Surg. *5*:34-40, 1971.

Hutton, C. E. Patient's evaluation of surgical correction of prognathism: survey of 32 patients. J. Oral Surg. *25*:225-228, 1967.

Jensen, S. H. The psychosocial dimensions of oral and maxillofacial surgery: a critical review of the literature. J. Oral Surg. *36*:447-453, 1978.

Knorr, N. J., M. T. Edgerton and J. E. Hoopes. The "insatiable" cosmetic surgery patient. Plast. Reconstr. Surg. *40*:285-289, 1967.

Knorr, N. J., J. E. Hoopes and M. T. Edgerton. Psychiatric-surgical approach to adolescent disturbance in self-image. Plast. Reconstr. Surg. *41*:285-289, 1968.

Laufer, D., D. Glick, D. Gutman and A. Sharon. Patient motivation and response to surgical correction of prognathism. Oral Surg. *41*:309, 1976.

LeJour, M. and C. LeCocq. Psychological implications of cosmetic surgery. Plast. Reconstr. Surg. *56*:603, 1975.

MacGregor, F. C. *After Plastic Surgery, Adaptation and Adjustment.* Praeger, 1979, New York, N.Y.

MacGregor, F. C., T. M. Abel, A. Bryt, E. Lauer and S. Weissman. *Facial Deformities and Plastic Surgery — A Psychosocial Study.* Charles Thomas (ed.), Springfield, Ill., 1953.

Molinaro, J. R. The social fate of children disfigured by burns. Am. J. Psychiatry. *135*:979-980, 1978.

Murray, J. E., L. T. Swanson, R. D. Strand and G. H. Hricko. Evaluation of craniofacial surgery in the treatment of facial deformities. Ann. Surg. *182*:240-265, 1975.

Olley, P. C. Aspects of plastic surgery — social and psychological sequelae. Brit. Med. J. *3*:322-324, 1974.

Osgood, C., Suci, G. J. and Tannenbaum, P. H. *The Measurement of Meaning* Urbana: University of Illinois Press, 1957.

Ouellette, P. L. Psychological ramifications of facial change in relation to orthodontic treatment and orthognathic surgery. J. Oral Surg. *36*:787-790, 1978.

Peterson, L. J. and R. G. Topazian. Psychological considerations in corrective maxillary and midfacial surgery. J. Oral Surg. *34*:157-164, 1976.

Reich, J. Factors influencing patient satisfaction with the results of esthetic plastic surgery. Esthetic Surg. *55*:1, 1975.

Reiner, M. L. Rehabilitation of the facially disfigured: a psychological analysis. Ann. Dent. *36*:29-34,1972.

Snyder, M., E. D. Tanke and E. Berscheid. Social perception and interpersonal behavior. On the self-fulfilling notions of social stereotypes. J. Personal. & Soc. Psych. *35*:656-666, 1977.

Stricker, G., E. Clifford, L. K. Cohen, D. B. Giddon, L. H. Meskin and C. A. Evans. Psychosocial aspects of craniofacial disfigurement. Am. J. Orthodont. *76*:410-422, 1979.

Wictorin, L., K. Hillerstrom and S. Sorenson. Biological and psychosocial factors in patients with malformation of the jaws. Scand. J. Plast. Reconstr. Surg. *3*:138-143, 1969.

Wilcox, J. Motivation toward and postoperative satisfaction with cosmetic oral surgery. Univ. of Texas, Dental Branch at Houston, 1972. Unpublished Master's Thesis.

Zuckerman, M. The development of an affect adjective check list for the measurement of anxiety. J. Consult. Psychol., *24*:457-462, 1960.

PSYCHOLOGICAL ADAPTATION OF PATIENTS WITH CRANIOFACIAL MALFORMATIONS

Kathy Kapp-Simon, M.A.

Center for Craniofacial Anomalies and Department of Psychiatry
University of Illinois

The phrase "craniofacial malformations" includes within its domain a wide spectrum of birth defects. These birth defects vary extensively in the degree to which they affect physical appearance. For example, congenital palatal insufficiency and isolated cleft palate have little stigmatizing effect on physical appearance, while the effects of cleft lip, mandibulofacial dysostosis, hypertelorism, Crouzon's disease and Apert's syndrome range from mild facial deformity to grotesque deformity which can affect not only facial appearance, but hands and feet as well. Consequently, efforts to understand psychological adaptation in patients with craniofacial anomalies must take into account the varying degrees to which these patients are affected, as well as the meaning that a particular defect has to an individual patient.

ATTRIBUTION OF MEANING

MacGregor and co-workers ('53) in their classic study suggested that, as a group, patients with severe facial deformities were more resigned and less bitter than those with mild deformities. They also stated, however, that even when patients were affected with the same type and degree of deformity, they differed markedly in their attitudes and overall adaptation. This differing reaction may be related to the meaning which a physical deformity has to the individual patient. Pivotal in understanding the attribution of meaning by a patient to his physical deformity is the psychological concept of body image. Body image can be defined as one aspect of self-concept which centers on an individual's perception of his/her own body. Two major components of body image include 1) body sense—the way an individual actually looks to himself when he looks in a mirror—and 2) body concept or conceptual image—the perceptions, thoughts, and feelings which an individual has in reference to viewing his/her own body which are an outgrowth of personal emotional experiences (Reich, '69; Schonfeld, '69; Peterson and Topazian, '76). Belfer and co-workers ('79) identified four factors which influence the development of body image, three of which are useful in expanding upon the components described above. These include: 1) the cognitive abilities of the patient which define the parameters of his/her body image development, 2) the sense of sameness or differentness which grows out of the patient's comparison of his/her body with those of the people in his/her environment, and 3) the responses or feedback the patient receives from the people in his/her environment which influence the types of value judgments he/she places upon the physical deformity. Meaning as determined by body image thus functions as a cognitive nucleus which influences the emotional significance of deformity for an individual. It is this emotional significance, rather than the degree of deformity, which has the more pronounced effect on an individual's ability to adopt adequate coping behaviors.

A case vignette is illustrative. One patient, who has been followed by our craniofacial team since birth, is the youngest of three girls in her family and the only child affected with a birth defect, a unilateral cleft lip and palate. Her father is more severely affected with a bilateral cleft lip and palate.

As a child, the scar from her cleft lip surgery was quite noticeable. Her lips were noticeably uneven, and there was a thickness due to bunching of muscles on the side of the cleft. Following a lip revision at age fifteen, however, the scarring diminished considerably. She was left with a slightly visible hairline scar on her upper lip and some very minimal unevenness of the vermillion border.

This patient had looked forward to the surgery at age 15 with great eagerness. She had lived with self-consciousness and the sense of being scarred or "imperfect" all of her young life and had anticipated that this final surgery would wipe away the residual evidence of her clefting. When this did not happen, she was extremely disappointed.

Objectively, this patient's surgical correction was very good. In addition, she had the advantage of a very animated face, which attracted attention to her total face rather than to the very minor scar on her lip.

For this patient, however, the fact that her lip was scarred pervaded her entire self-perception. When talking or laughing she frequently covered the scarred side of her mouth with her hand. When meeting people for the first time she always anticipated rejection.

In spite of her preoccupation with her cleft, however, she was not socially isolated. She had a group of loyal friends, many of whom actively tried to diminish her self-consciousness by affirming her likableness. She also dated; but here, too, she lived in continual fear of rejection. For example, she would refuse to meet male friends of her boyfriend for fear they would laugh at him for dating such an ugly girl.

By age sixteen she had dropped out of high school so that she would not have to deal with people; she had become sexually active to hold a boyfriend and then despised herself for doing it. She was unable to hold a job—when tension developed between her and her supervisors, she would quit rather than work out the issues. She could see how she used her cleft as an excuse, yet she felt powerless to initiate changes in her behavior. To this girl, her cleft symbolized her own feelings of being different and inadequate. Though objectively a minor defect, it loomed large in her eyes as a major force influencing her life.

This patient's experience points to an important factor which must be considered when examining the psychological consequences of craniofacial birth defects. Medical treatment for the correction of these birth defects takes place in stages often beginning soon after birth and not reaching completion until the patient is nearly an adult. For the patient with minor anomalies, e.g., cleft lip and palate, the goal which is held out to the family is "almost normalcy". For patients with more severe anomalies, the goal is less clear, but always implied as part of it is improved appearance in order to make the patient "socially acceptable".

MINOR CRANIOFACIAL ANOMALIES

When parents bring their infant to a clinic for the treatment of cleft lip and palate, they are told that the infant's lip will be closed as soon as he/she is strong enough to withstand the surgery (8 to 10 lbs.) and that the palate will be closed as soon as there is enough tissue (twelve to eighteen months of age). They are also told that as the child develops, his/her lip may grow unevenly and that additional surgery can later correct the disparities that develop. Generally, it is postulated that the habilitation process will be completed when growth is complete, sometime between the ages of fifteen and seventeen. At that point, the final definitive cosmetic correction of the cleft will occur. Thus, for the child with a cleft there are many periods of waiting—"in-between-times" (Bettleheim, '50)—between first surgery and age seventeen when he/she must cope with anticipatory hopes and fears regarding future treatment, as well as the often unsatisfactory appearance of his/her present self. It is during these years that fantasies about the final outcome develop.

It is unfortunate, but true, that individuals with craniofacial malformations are immediately recognizable. Thus, when a child with residual scarring from a cleft lip enters school for the first time he/she often meets with questions, stares, or teasing. In Goffman's ('63) terms, the process of stigmatization occurs concurrently with the socialization process inherent in the educational system.

One study investigated the effects of early socialization on the self-concept of children between the ages of five and eight who had cleft lip and/or palate (Kapp, '79). The results of this study are alarming. As a

145

group, the cleft children, regardless of sex, reported significantly more self-concept disturbance than would be expected compared to the normative data and to a random sample of local noncleft children.

Two factors contributed to the lowered scores for the cleft children: emotional self and social self as measured by this study. With regard to the emotional self factor, children with clefts more often identified with a child who was unhappy or crying than with a child who was happy. The most common reason given for the tears was that someone would not allow them to join in a game.

With regard to the social self factor, children with clefts reported that they played alone significantly more frequently than did the children in the control group. Some of the cleft children spontaneously made statements such as "I always play alone, the other kids don't want me to play." Others stated after questioning that they were often teased and chased away by the other children. However, when the score for helpfulness, the second domain of the social self factor, was studied, the possibility that the cleft children lacked some of the skills necessary for reciprocal play with their agemates became evident. Many of the cleft children saw themselves more consistently receiving from, rather than giving to, their playmates, e.g., they were the ones to receive a ride in the wagon rather than give it; they were the ones to receive a piggy back ride rather than the ones to give it. It is also possible that this lowered helpfulness score reflects not only the cleft child's overidentification with the one needing to be taken care of, but also a corollary lack of belief in their own ability to be helpful.

A natural follow-up of the above study would be to investigate the parents' and teachers' perceptions of the social and emotional adjustment of young children with clefts. Data from both parents and teachers were available for thirty-two of the fifty children included in the above study. The following statements were used to assess parent and teacher perception of emotional adjustment:

Child cries more easily than most children.

Child complains frequently about headaches, stomachaches, or dizziness.

Child is self-conscious about appearance.

Child is uneasy about new things or going to new places.

The following statements were used to assess parent and teacher perception of social self:

Child generally spends free time alone.

Child has difficulty making or keeping friends.

Child gets into frequent fights or quarrels with playmates.

Child is teased more frequently than most children.

Low, but significant, positive correlations were found when parent and teacher evaluations of the children's emotional state were compared with the children's self reports. That is, parent and child evaluations correlated at .39 (p<.02), and the teacher and child evaluations correlated at .32 (p<.04). However, the correlation of parent-teacher reports with each other was insignificant (.05). Both parents and teachers were aware of the emotional difficulties some of the children were having, but they did not agree as to the nature or cause of these difficulties.

On the social behavior measure neither parent nor teacher agreed with the child's perception of his social self, nor did parent and teacher agree with each other. It is difficult to interpret this discrepancy in viewpoint without further data. It may be that parents and teachers are not always aware of the times when children with clefts are excluded from peer activities, or perhaps the frequency is not as great as the children's report might indicate. It may simply be that the child's subjective experience of rejection or exclusion is based on a limited (but powerful) number of occasions. This view was given some support by at least one parent, who stated that she knew her little boy *felt* rejected by his agemates even though he spent a great deal of time playing with them.

On the other hand, in support of the child's perception, one mother recently described the experience of watching her daughter's first grade class playing organized games under the teacher's supervision. (The child's home is directly in back of the school, and the mother stated she could not be seen by the children). As a game of "duck, duck, goose" proceeded, this mother saw each child in turn be picked to be a runner, except her daughter. As the mother watched, some children began receiving a second turn, and still her daughter had not been picked. Fortuitously, or perhaps out of an awareness of what was happening, the teacher at that point introduced a game of "follow the leader".

This, unfortunately, was not an isolated incident. By the end of two weeks in the first grade, this little girl, who had a bilateral cleft lip and palate, cried about having to go to school. She enjoyed her classes but had not been able to make one friend. She was pushed away from the play equipment at recess time and was not invited to join in group activities with her classmates.

It is experiences like these which contribute to the stigmatization process and which can make the "in-between" years for children with cleft lip and palate difficult. Such experiences can lead to the attribution of negative meaning by a child to his/her cleft and can also lead to fantasies about how things could be different if the scars were not there. Thus, a common wish among cleft children is to blend in or to not be noticed. For many of these patients the final surgery becomes the last chance to achieve that hoped for anonymity.

Even when overall adjustment has been good, as in the following case (Kapp, '78), there is a sense that this surgery will have major impact. At age sixteen, in her frustration over not having dates like her sister, one patient emphatically stated that it was hurtful for her to think that after surgery (referring to the final surgery that was to be performed at age seventeen) when she wouldn't look like she did now, the boys might decide to go out with her. She imagined the boys saying "You know, it's all right to go out with her now. She had surgery and she doesn't look like she did before." The paradox of this patient's case highlights the no-win situation that even children who have achieved emotional stability may face.

MAJOR CRANIOFACIAL ANOMALIES

The treatment of patients with more severe forms of craniofacial malformations has undergone dramatic changes as new surgical techniques have been developed in recent years. Therefore, the attempts to assess the psychological impact of surgical intervention is, in many ways, a virgin field.

The following discussion will be divided into two sections reflecting the advent of specific advanced surgical procedures developed by Tessier in 1973 and used by Schafer on a regular basis within the last two years. The first part of the discussion will look at Dr. Tessier's patients who underwent surgery six to seven years ago, and the second will look at Dr. Schafer's patients, all of whom were operated on within the last two years.

Preliminary Research Findings

Unlike the parents' of children with cleft lip and palate, the parents of children with more severe forms of craniofacial malformations were not, until recently, given much hope for the correction of their child's physical appearance. Until the advent of Tessier's approaches to these problems, little could be done to correct the structural problems which were the bases of the deformities of these patients. The fact that professionals could not provide these parents with hope did not mean, however, that they had given up hope. These parents were fighters. They had refused to institutionalize their children as was recommended to many of them when their children were born, and they did not give up hope that help would some day become available. Clifford ('74) described these parents as follows:

At times parents may go from practitioner to practitioner and from agency to agency seeking a source of help. Frequently this search is accompanied by a belief in medical progress, and the hope that what cannot be accomplished now will be accomplished in the future. . . . They are strong advocates of intervention, seeking cures and palliatives. Some quickly become aware of new techniques and desparately seek them for their children, frequently using sophisticated terminology and speaking learnedly of procedures.

The patients originally operated on by Dr. Tessier were evaluated pre- and, within a short time, post-surgically (Clifford, '74). The majority of the children were adolescents at the time of surgery, and Clifford's data reflects information gathered primarily from that group. The evaluation included an assessment of maternal attitude toward the child and an assessment of the child's perception of parental attitude, as well as some measures of satisfaction with appearance pre- and post-surgery.

Clifford ('74) found that mothers of patients with craniofacial anomalies reported more negative feelings about the birth of these children than do mothers of normal children. Specifically, they reported significantly less pride in their children and greater apprehension about caring for them as infants. These mothers also rated their children's current appearance far more negatively than did mothers of normal children. Facial appearance was reported to be totally unacceptable. Clifford found that these negative ratings carried over to the mothers' evaluations of their children's personality and level of functioning as well.

Through the evaluation of these children with craniofacial anomalies, Clifford discovered that they *did* perceive their parents as having predominantly negative reactions to them since the time of their birth; however, unlike the parents, these children did not perceive a spread effect. These children felt that, in spite of their parents' worry and apprehension, they did take pride in them and were able to nurture them in a warm and caring way. Clifford suggests that the disparity between the parents' feelings and the children's perceptions of their parents' feelings may indicate either that the parents were able to overcome their negative feelings to the extent that they were able show enough pride and nurturance to create a perception of acceptance on the part of the children, or that the children simply could not face and, hence, verbalize a perception of lack of nurturance and pride on the part of their parents.

Since most of the patients operated on by Tessier were fifteen years or older at the time of surgery, they had already developed ways of coping with their malformation. This lead Clifford to question the role of the malformation in the individual's life and to hypothesize that "the longer the person has had to accommodate to the craniofacial malformation, all other things being equal, the greater is the dependence upon the malformation. Further, it may also be stated that "the greater the dependence upon the malformation, the greater the disintegration experienced with its removal" (Clifford, '74).

When Clifford questioned Tessier's patients about their expectations of craniofacial surgery, two themes emerged. One major expectation of both parents and patients was that pervasive behavioral changes would occur as a result of the surgery. "In some cases, there was no area of the behavior of the child which would *not* change with the contemplated surgery." Other staff members retrospectively stated that a mood of expectation was shared by many on the staff as well. There was an excitement surrounding the surgery, perhaps arising out of the belief that, at last, the clinic was able to offer something substantial in the way of corrective surgery to these patients. Certainly, most of the staff expected dramatic physical changes from the surgery and then anticipated that behavioral changes, at least in the area of social acceptance, would follow.

The second theme which emerged from Clifford's interviews concerned patients' fantasies about changes in their appearance. Many patients imagined that after surgery they would not be recognized by parents or friends. The removal of the facial malformations which, especially for the adolescents, had for so long played a major role in the presentation of self, can and does raise questions about the loss of self-identification. This whole question will be addressed later in this presentation.

Longitudinal Clinical Evaluations

In evaluating the outcome of surgery for these patients, several factors must be taken into consideration: 1) age; 2) level of adjustment at time of surgical intervention; 3) degree of objective improvement from surgery; 4) subjective evaluation of improvement by patient and families; and 5) adjustment of patient to new appearance, e.g., ability to cope with new social responses from environment.

Two broad categories of patients can be identified using the above criteria. The first category includes those for whom the surgery removed the disfigurement, thus enabling them to move in society without drawing negative attention to themselves. For these patients, the surgery removed the external stigma and fulfilled the wish of many of them to blend into a group or not to stand out as different. Five of the twenty patients operated on by Dr. Tessier fit into this category. Four were female, two were under eight years of age and two were young adults, ages eighteen and twenty-four respectively. The male was fifteen years of age at the time of surgery and had an extremely mild presurgical hypertelorism. The second group of patients consists of those for whom surgery altered their appearance, generally enabling them to more closely approximate normal appearance, but not enabling them to blend unnoticed in a crowd. The majority of Dr. Tessier's patients, fifteen out of twenty, fell into this group.

Effects of Surgical Intervention. One patient was five years of age when she was operated on for hypertelorism. She had no other malformations, and as her midline scar faded, becoming nearly invisible some years following surgery, this patient at twelve years of age had no easily recognizable indications of her earlier anomaly. Her classmates had no knowledge of her birth defect, since there were no signs to lead them to ask the question dreaded by so many with craniofacial birth defects, "What happened to you?" When interviewing this patient, it became clear that her birth defect did not play a major role in her life. She had no readily available memories of the years before age five, when she would have stood out in a group, and thus does not identify herself as someone "different" from her classmates. When teased about her small pug nose, as occasionally happens, her quick reply is that she has a nose like her mother's which, in fact, is true. For this patient, corrective surgery provided her with a strong family resemblance.

For an eighteen-year-old patient, corrective surgery resulted in a completely transformed appearance. Using make-up effectively to camouflage the residual scarring, this young woman changed from an ugly outcast to an attractive and socially desirable young woman. Unfortunately, she did not possess the social skills which would have enabled her to cope with her new status. She found herself uncomfortable, though flattered, by the male attention she now received. She began a rather whirlwind dating circuit which culminated in her marrying a man she had dated only a few times. She soon discovered that the man she had married was a transvestite, and she found herself feeling both angry and trapped. Though she finally succeeded in obtaining a divorce, she was left feeling abused and vulnerable. She is far more cautious now in her relationships, for she has been scarred in a way which, though less visible, is none-the-less permeating.

The contrast in adjustment between the five-year-old and the eighteen-year-old suggests that even when surgical outcome is ideal, patients who have lived many years with their deformity may need assistance in adjusting to their changed status in society.

More important than objective physical change is the effect the change has on the individual's self-perception. A positively modified self-perception can result in more assertive and adaptive self-presentation. In turn, this may lead to experimentation with new social skills and a more confident self-projection. These changes may reorder the social responses of the environment and reinforce adaptive social development. Particularly with the young child, if significant others in the nurturing environment share in a new perception of greater attractiveness, they may structure their approaches to the child in a way more likely to imbue positive self-concept and thus foster the development of healthy personal adjustment.

Assessment of adjustment and a determination of the results of craniofacial surgery are far less clear cut for the majority of patients with severe craniofacial anomalies, as they are left with residual evidence of their anomaly. Thus, for these patients, post-surgical adjustment involves adapting to a changed, but still deviant, appearance.

Perhaps the most striking example of the difficulties faced by these patients can be seen in the case of a twenty-year-old male who underwent three separate surgical procedures for the correction of his anomaly. Though surgery resulted in a dramatic improvement, he was far from normal in appearance and could never blend into a social situation. Clifford ('74) described this patient's immediate post-surgical reactions as follows:

> Before surgery, strangers assumed he had a birth defect and rarely asked him about it. After surgery, people were asking him whether he had been in an accident. He felt the easy way out would be to agree that he was in an accident. He also felt that this explanation provided a cop-out for him; it was a way of avoiding the real explanation. He was reacting to the necessity of changing his defensive posture. Other behaviors were also undergoing change, for his mother reported that he no longer was as independent as he had been prior to surgery. She reported that he was exhibiting more fear in selected social situations.

Time did not improve this patient's adjustment. The years following surgery were characterized by much personal conflict and increasing tension in family relations. The patient attempted to resume his college education but had great difficulty in completing a semester. He would register for a full course load and then one by one drop the courses. Dropping courses was only one symbol of this patient's need to escape. Periodically, he would just pick up and disappear. He reported hitchhiking to California and enjoying the anonymity of being a wanderer. Always he returned, however, and at age twenty-five he had accumulated enough credits to be awarded a bachelor's degree.

When speaking about his surgical experience, this patient raised some thought-provoking concerns. On more than one occasion he stated that he regretted agreeing to the surgeries, that he felt he had violated himself by submitting to the surgery. He explained that all of his life he had been told to accept himself, that personality was more important than appearance, and that he had a lot to contribute to society simply by being who he was. When the opportunity for surgery came along, he was given different messages by his family and by the professionals responsible for his treatment. He was told surgery would make him more acceptable to society and he would have a better chance to make something of himself if he looked better. The societal conflict, so skillfully outlined by Berscheid ('80) is personified in this patient. He wanted desperately to believe those who in his youth had told him that beauty wasn't important. Yet, these same people were the ones who urged him to undergo the surgery, thus implying that beauty was important after all. The final consequence for this patient appears to be a fractured self-concept and confusion in personal identity which necessitated a refashioning of the structure of his coping skills and defensive system while delaying a permanent transition into adult identity and responsibility. He continues to flounder in a no-man's land, unemployed and without social ties.

Not all patients react the way that the twenty year-old man in the above vignette did. The next two case histories illustrate two different reactions to quite similar surgical outcomes. Both patients are female, have Crouzon's disease and were in their early 20's at the time of surgical intervention.

The first patient was twenty-four at the time of intervention. She had completed college and was a special education instructor. Like other patients, although she hoped for improved appearance, a major motivating factor for surgery was protection of her eyes. Surgery was successful in providing protection for her eyes. However, an undesirable outcome of the surgery was that her large nose was accentuated and her face remained quite unattractive. Her eyes now appear somewhat sunken, and there is a tautness to her skin which is unnatural. However, this woman's carriage and personality belies her objective appearance. She is bubbly, enthusiastic, and self-confident. In the seven years following surgery she obtained a master's degree in special education and is now director of special education in her school district. This woman has an active social life, though until recently, her relationships with men have been casual. This is somewhat disappointing to her since she would like to marry; however, she is still hopeful that she will meet the right person. In the meantime, she is living her life to its fullness without self-pity.

The second case history is of a woman who was twenty-five at the time of surgery. She was employed full time and lived independent of her family. Her acquaintances were primarily female peers, and she had negligible dating experiences. Like the first patient, a primary goal for surgery was the protection of her eyes, which protruded extensively and were extremely red and irritated. However, a strong underlying hope and expectation was that surgery would enhance her appearance, making her acceptable to men, and thus transform her social life completely. The dates which would follow would then free her from the loneliness she felt and would allow her to lead the more normal existence she craved. The surgical results, which were acceptable from an objective standpoint, did not meet her expectations. While the protrusion of her eyes was partially corrected, evidence of her birth defect remained. Unlike the first patient, however, this patient's reaction was depression. When the hoped-for dates did not materialize, she began bar hopping to attract attention. She also began consuming large amounts of alcohol, frequently drinking when alone at home. The pattern of drinking and depression have continued throughout the seven years following surgery. So far, she has maintained her job and is currently up for a promotion. She recognizes, however, that her current behavior is self-destructive, and she is unsure how long she can continue her dual existence — lonely alcoholic at night and respectable employee by day. Recently she sought help. Only time will tell if she can begin to reshape her personal life in a way which is meaningful and satisfying to her.

A major theme illustrated by the contrasting history of these two patients is that for older patients, presurgical adjustment is an indicator of postsurgical adaption. The first patient had achieved a satisfactory life adjustment prior to surgery. While she anticipated and welcomed an improved appearance, her hopes for happiness and personal satisfaction were not tied to, nor dependent on, that improvement. In contrast, the second patient expected the results of the surgery to make a major difference in her personal life and happiness. When this did not happen, she lacked the internal resources to maintain even the level of adjustment which was present prior to surgery.

A third case history, that of a young woman with Crouzon's disease, provides another perspective on psychological adaptation. This patient was also twenty-four years old at the time of surgery. Unlike the two patients previously described, however, this woman focused on her facial deformity as a totally incapacitating factor in her life. She continued to live with her parents and was totally dependent on them financially. She had never held a job and firmly believed she would never obtain a job as long as she looked the way she did. (Interestingly, from an objective standpoint, this patient was less severely affected than either of the first two presented above.) This patient had a limited social life and was extremely self-conscious in public. She was also bitter about her lot in life and firm in her belief that a total change in every aspect of her life would occur following reconstructive surgery.

This patient was not part of the original craniofacial study but was operated on four years later. Thus, the staff was aware of some of the post-surgical emotional difficulties encountered by patients, particularly when the results do not meet their expectations either in terms of improved appearance or in terms of anticipated social changes. As a result, efforts were made, through presurgery psychological counseling, to help this patient develop more realistic goals and expectations for surgery. Some minor, but definite, progress was made through the counseling; however, it was still felt that this patient was at risk for post-surgical depression, and it was determined that supportive services would be maintained in the post-surgical period.

This patient's immediate post-surgical period was characterized by much complaining and an attitude of helplessness. For four months following surgery, she sat around and let her family wait on her. Although she expressed satisfaction with her changed appearance, she was mildly depressed and reluctant to socialize outside of her home.

Prior to surgery, this patient had been enrolled in a vocational training program, and by the fifth month after surgery the agency was pressuring her to go on job interviews. She resisted them but decided on her own to respond to an ad for a cashier's job in a local department store. Working as a cashier was a dream of hers which, prior to surgery, she felt could never be realized because, by her logic, no manager would hire someone who looked the way she looked. Now, with her improved appearance (her surgical outcome was good), she was optimistic when she went for the job interview, and she was hired for the job. She has now worked successfully for three years, receiving regular raises and a promotion to manager of a department. For this patient, surgery was an important stepping stone. When she looked better, she was able to present herself more confidently and thus influence the ways in which people in her environment responded to her. Surgery did not solve all of her social/emotional problems, but it did enable her to change her self-identity from that of a helpless, deformed girl to that of a woman who could begin to take responsibility for herself.

Early Intervention

Recently, efforts have been made to provide children with the benefits of craniofacial surgery at as young an age as possible. A primary goal of this early intervention is minimization of the social and emotional difficulties which these children face when they are forced to live with their deformity through adolescence. The assumption underlying this goal is that improvement in appearance will have social payoffs which in turn will affect the emotional development of these children.

There are a number of factors, however, which must be taken into consideration when attempting to test this assumption:

1. What is the extent of physical improvement which can be anticipated through early surgical intervention? How many operations are needed to achieve the most satisfactory appearance? It is known that hospitalizations can have a negative effect on the emotional development of children. What is the effect of three to five surgeries over two or more years on a young child? Is it possible that the traumas of surgery and hospitalization can negate the potential benefits of the improvement in physical appearance?

2. Considering MacGregor's ('53) findings that patients with severe facial deformities are more resigned and less bitter than those with mild deformities, if we transform severe deformities into mild ones, do we run the risk of creating more bitter patients?

3. How do the patients and their families cope with the in-between-times, the months between surgical procedures? These times can be difficult as families are impatient to be finished, yet anxious about facing another bout of hospitalization with their child.

4. What will growth do to the child's appearance? Should we expect that, similar to cleft lip and palate children, growth will be uneven, thus bringing renewed attention to the deformity as the child matures?

To a large extent, these are unanswered questions because the longitudinal data is not yet available. Some hypotheses can be formulated, however, and some preliminary data based on current cases can be presented.

When early surgical intervention is successful in eliminating the visible stigmata of a craniofacial birth defect, it seems safe to assume that that child's chances for normal social/emotional development have been immensely improved. The case of the five-year-old girl with hypertelorism reported earlier is illustrative. Unfortunately, this kind of a case is rare, because most craniofacial deformities are not correctable in one operation as hers was, nor does surgery always achieve the same degree of success. So, more often the question is how do you measure the benefits of improved appearance? What is the effect of changing the child's appearance from extremely deviant to moderately or mildly deviant on the social/ emotional development of a child. Again, case histories can provide some clues.

The first case is that of a four-and-one-half-year-old girl who has a congenital absence of her nose and eyes of slightly unequal size. She is blind in the smaller eye. She is a bright, personable young girl who, on her first visit to our clinic at age four, wanted to know which of these people looking at her was going to give her a nose. This child knew, even at her young age, that she was different from other children, and she wanted something done about it. The surgical plan decided upon was to build up the available tissue by stretching the nasal area through implants under the skin. These implants would gradually be increased in size until enough tissue was available to begin to construct a nose.

At the time of this writing, the child has had one surgical procedure requiring a very brief (three days) hospital stay. The second procedure, requiring five to seven days of hospitalization, will occur in the immediate future. There will be about two months between procedures.

Following the first procedure, the child had a very slight bump on her face in the area of her nose. It was barely noticeable to the casual observer. The child, however, was ecstatic. On her first visit to the clinic following surgery, she ran across the waiting room, pointing to this tiny bump, saying, "Look, look, I've got a nose." Prior to this, her human figure drawings, while age appropriate, had always been missing a nose. On this day, she proudly and spontaneously drew a picture of herself with a nose. On subsequent visits, her drawings sometimes had a nose and sometimes didn't, suggesting that, understandably, this new part of her was not yet fully integrated. She herself said it best during one of the later interviews; when questioned about the missing nose on her drawing she paused, touched her little bump and said, "Oh, yah, I forgot."

Thus far, treatment has had a positive effect on this young girl. Though she cannot yet express it this way, getting a nose, even the suggestion of a nose, enables her to feel more like other people who have noses. What remains to be seen is the long term surgical outcome and her final evaluation of it.

The second patient was six years old at the time of her first major surgery. She had a congenital cleft lip, bilateral choanal atresia, hyperte-lorism and a bifid nose. One nostril was opened, and her cleft lip was closed late in her first year of life.

In spite of her unusual facial features, this little girl gave the impression of being a cute child. She was outgoing and possessed a delightful personality. Her mother tried to foster in her a belief that she was a beautiful person. Though she was at times teased by her peers, she did not verbal-ize a knowledge that she did, in fact, look different from other children.

The weeks following this child's first surgical procedure were difficult. She was withdrawn, did not engage in her normal play behavior and was enuretic. On occasion, she would pull a blanket or basket over her head, refusing to let herself be seen even by family members. Through play therapy interviews, it became clear that this child was having great diffi-culty integrating both the surgical experience and her own changed ap-pearance. Frequently, during therapy sessions, one puppet would ask the child puppet what had happened that she looked so different. For many weeks, the child puppet did not have an answer. Gradually, however, she began to recreate the surgery and to talk about fixing the puppet child's eyes (the puppet child always bore her own name). Soon after these verbalizations, her depression lifted and she was able to return to school.

Following the first surgery, this child did look different. The hypertelorism was corrected, and skin grafts were applied to her nose so that sufficient tissue would be available for nasal reconstruction during future surgeries. It would be difficult to say, however, that the total impression was one of improvement. Her nose was still most noticeably deformed, and the improvement in the relationship of her eyes was camouflaged by her glasses. Following this surgery, she continued to complain of teasing from her classmates.

About six months after the first surgery, a second procedure was performed. Only minor revisions were made at that time, however, because it was felt the skin grafts needed more time to "take".

Although she was quicker to bounce back from the second surgery, the actual hospitalization was more difficult the second time. Nightmares and restlessness were frequent, and on at least one occasion she cried in sleep, saying, "I want them to be done with my face."

At the time of writing, this child is awaiting her third surgery. Throughout this interim period, the in-between-times, teasing and name-calling has been a problem in the school. Although this girl is coping reasonably well, according to her teacher, she does frequently talk about how to handle the teasing. She does not, however, appear to relate the teasing to her nose in a way that indicates she expects it to stop when surgery on her nose is complete. Although she is a bright child, she has thus far only vaguely related the surgery to changes in her appearance.

Again, the findings on this case are not complete. It is obvious that the surgeries have been traumatic for this child; however, with therapy, she has been able to regain a sense of herself and is once again vivacious and outgoing. In spite of the disruptions of surgery, she has been able to maintain her academic performance at a high level.

These two cases are representative of the cases currently followed at our Center, and the preliminary data suggest that through the initial stages of reconstruction, these children can be helped to maintain a level of adjustment commensurate with their presurgical state. A number of the children need assistance in coming to terms with a changing identity and may experience temporary setbacks, as did the second girl described above. It is crucial, therefore, that craniofacial teams provide psychological services to these children throughout the process of reconstruction. Contact should be maintained between surgeries as well as during the times immediately surrounding surgery, because often the strong feelings do not emerge until the healing process is well under way and the immediate crisis is over.

As yet, no definite answers can be given to the questions raised about long term benefits. We have not followed the children long enough. It is clear, however, that for most of the children, diminishing the severity of the deformity in itself does not extinguish the teasing of peers. Therefore, the children will still be potential victims of the stigmatization process. It is not unreasonable to assume that some of these patients will be bitter about having put themselves through so much only to meet rejection because still they were different. It can be hoped, however, that the majority will find their new appearance more comfortable to live with than the old and, therefore, be able to find ways of adaptively coping with the stigmatization which still occurs.

CONCLUSIONS

This exploration of the psychological aspects of facial surgery points to the urgent need for further research in so many of these areas. While progress has been made in understanding the social and emotional problems these patients face, there are still many unanswered questions.

The case examples presented should remind us of the necessity of understanding the uniqueness of each child's social and emotional capacities for adaptation to deformity and to corrective surgery. It is impossible to separate the physical surgery from its personal and interpersonal consequences. In a unique way, the altering of facial appearance affects identity and self-concept. We need to better understand the psychological processes which play a pivotal role in identity transformation. The challenge is to understand how patients with differing deformities, varying levels of personal adjustment, and differing personality styles are able to benefit from—and cope with—the effects of surgery. Understanding these relationships will enable us to facilitate the development of individually successful coping styles through pre-operative, post-operative, and long-term follow-up counseling. Hopefully, we can then more consistently alleviate some of the pain related to social stigmatization.

REFERENCES

Belfer, M., A. Harrison and J. Murray. Body image and the process reconstructive surgery. Unpublished manuscript, 1979.

Berscheid, E. An overview of the psychological effects of physical attractiveness. In: *Psychological Aspects of Facial Form* (W. Lucker, K. Ribbens and J. A. McNamara, Jr., eds.), Monograph No. 11, Craniofacial Growth Series, Center for Human Growth and Development, The University of Michigan, Ann Arbor, 1981.

Bettelheim, B. *Love is Not Enough.* The Free Press, New York, 1950.

Clifford, E. Insights and speculations: Psychological exploration of the craniofacial experience. Paper presented at the Conference on the Evaluation of Recent Advances in Craniofacial Surgery. Chicago, 1974.

Goffman, E. *Stigma*. Prentice-Hall, Englewood Cliffs, New Jersey, 1963.

Kapp, K. *A Child With a Difference*. Videotape. University of Illinois Medical Center, Chicago, 1978.

Kapp, K. Self-concept of primary level children with clefts. Paper presented at 36th Annual Meeting of the American Cleft Palate Association, San Diego, Ca., 1979.

MacGregor, F. C., T. M. Abel, A. Bryt, E. Lauer and S. Weissman. *Facial Deformities and Plastic Surgery: A psychosocial study*. Charles C. Thomas, Springfield, Ill., 1953.

Peterson, L. and R. Topazian. Psychological considerations in corrective maxillary and midfacial surgery. J. Oral Surg *34*:157-164, 1976.

Reich, J. The surgery of appearance: Psychological and related aspects. Med. J. Austral., pp. 5-13, 1969.

Schonfeld, W. The body and the body-image in adolescents. In: *Adolescence Psychosocial Perspectives*. Basic Books, Inc., New York, 1969.

PSYCHOLOGICAL EVALUATION OF THE ORTHOGNATHIC SURGICAL PATIENT

Robert C. Colligan, M.D., Ph.D.

Associate Professor of Psychology, Mayo Medical School
Consultant, Mayo Clinic and Mayo Foundation

A. Howard Sather, D.D.S.

Associate Professor of Dentistry, Mayo Medical School
Consultant, Mayo Clinic and Mayo Foundation

Michael C. Hollen, D.D.S.

Resident in Orthodontics
Mayo Graduate School of Medicine

During the past several years, the number of patients being treated for dentofacial deformities through a combined treatment of orthodontics and surgery has increased dramatically. This increase is a reflection of several factors. Increased awareness of cosmetic procedures by health professionals and the public-at-large has led larger numbers of individuals to seek reconstructive therapy. More extensive third-party coverage of medical costs has provided more opportunity for individuals who have been held back for financial reasons. Improvement in surgical techniques and treatment technologies has improved results and thereby increased practitioner confidence in tackling more difficult cases. However, the largest part of the increase in demand for reconstructive therapy must be attributed to the increased value placed on appearance by contemporary society.

The particular importance placed on a pleasing facial appearance by society is reflected by the results of a classic study by Richardson and colleagues ('61), in which 640 boys and girls, aged ten and eleven years, who came from diverse social and cultural backgrounds, were asked to rank six photographs of other children from most liked to least liked. The results showed that the photograph of the child with a disfigurement near his mouth was less liked than photographs of children with crutches, in wheelchairs, or with missing hands. The values and prejudices displayed by these children toward facial disfigurement reflect the values and prejudices of their adult environment. MacGregor ('66) stated that the face is

161

the most important means of self-identification and self-presentation of a person in everyday life. This fact becomes apparent when one analyzes the time and investment a person spends on facial care, as compared with care for other parts of the body.

The effects of physical attractiveness on the socialization process are addressed in this volume by Adams, who describes several controlled studies that underscore previous reports that facial disfigurements have a negative influence both on the person with the disfigurement and on society around him/her. Munro reports elsewhere in this volume that although some of his patients on initial interview indicated that they desired correction of a deformity for functional reasons, subsequent and more comprehensive interviews revealed that improved appearance was the primary reason for seeking care.

The results of all studies to date have documented the importance of having an acceptable appearance in the development of the personality and in the availability of opportunities to a person in society. The appearance of the teeth, the appearance of the jaw, and the position and function of the soft tissue of the face (lip posture, smile line, etc.) are all important factors to be considered by any team providing orthognathic surgical care. Fortunately, within the dentofacial complex, the correction of a deformity of occlusion, skeletal relationship, or soft-tissue structure undertaken to satisfy physiological functional needs also results in improved facial balance and dental aesthetics.

Rigid social standards concerning facial appearance place excessive pressures on people whose appearance deviates from normal. This societal pressure was responsible for the reactions of most plastic surgery patients investigated in a study by MacGregor ('66). These patients had a broad spectrum of psychological disorders, including serious mental illness. When facial disfigurement was encountered, evaluations of that person were negative and stigmatizing. If the facial disfigurement was acquired at an age when the patient had already developed prejudices toward such disfigurements, these same attitudes were self-directed. The primary emotional disturbance encountered in a group studied by Pilling (in press) was anxiety, which can result in emotional disorders ranging from phobias to psychoses. Thus, the facially disfigured person may also become psychologically disfigured as a result of society's attitude of disapproval.

PERSONALITY EVALUATION

The psychosomatic model of patient care stresses the importance of evaluating both psychological and physiological factors in patients. It is estimated that 50% to 70% of the patients in a physician's general practice have significant psychological problems; the need for a holistic view of the patient is obvious. However, such evaluation cannot be routinely handled by referral to psychiatrists or psychologists.

MMPI

In order to obtain information about social-emotional functioning from patients, a number of structured psychological tests have been developed. The most well-researched of these objective personality questionnaires is the Minnesota Multiphasic Personality Inventory (MMPI). The MMPI is composed of 550 statements about life experiences, physical and emotional symptoms, attitudes, feelings, and ideas to which a patient must respond "true" or "false". In general, the material included in the MMPI would ordinarily be covered during a lengthy clinical interview. However, the privacy afforded by paper-and-pencil administration, the economy of administration time compared with that required for thorough interviewing by a skilled clinician, and the usefulness of the information provided have all contributed to the acceptance of the MMPI as a screening measure and as a clinical tool in health care settings. In a survey of 158 physicians, 87% described the information obtained from the MMPI as reinforcing the confidence they placed in their clinical evaluation of the patient's emotional status (Swenson et al., '65). In addition, 65% reported that information from the MMPI revealed emotional problems of an unsuspected kind or degree. Evaluation of psychological factors is also believed to have been valuable in the rehabilitation of patients who had maxillofacial defects corrected by a prosthesis (Gillis et al., '79).

The MMPI is basically a self-report inventory. Such questionnaires have been used for years to obtain information about the ideas, perceptions, and feelings of patients. However, the early questionnaires had many weaknesses with regard to assessment of personality functioning because the intent of the examiner was usually obvious. Responses could be intentionally biased and, therefore, not validly represent the responder's true opinions. The MMPI represented a major improvement because the items selected for inclusion were identified by empirical means rather than by the speculations of mental health workers or theories of personality development.

As originally conceived, the MMPI was intended to yield information about personality factors related to the major psychiatric syndromes. Responses to the statements are scored along ten scales that represent important components of personality functioning. The items composing each scale were validated statistically. An item was included only if a carefully diagnosed group of patients (for example, those hospitalized for depression) answered that question in a statistically different manner from other groups with reliably diagnosed conditions (for example, schizophrenic patients) and from a normal control group. This system of item selection led to the inclusion of both obvious and subtle questions. Thus, Scale 2 (Depression) includes obvious items which logically might relate to a scale measuring depression, such as, "I wish I could be as happy as others seem to be" (to which depressed patients tend to answer "true") but also items for which intuitive explanations for inclusion are virtually impossible. For example, depressed patients tend to respond "false" to the item "I sweat very easily, even on cool days." Because the MMPI includes both types of items, it is more reliable and valid than many other self-assessment devices.

In addition, a set of four scales, commonly called the validity scales, has been developed to inform the examiner about factors in the patient's response style which might influence the validity of the MMPI. These four scales provide indications about literacy, level of cooperation, tendency toward malingering, comprehension of the task, psychological defensiveness, and so on.

The MMPI is not suitable for children, but it can be used with adolescents from approximately the age of fourteen years. Adults must have a reading ability and general comprehension level equal to or greater than (approximately) the sixth grade level.

After a patient has responded to the statements of the MMPI, the answers are scored either by hand or by computer. A number of computerized scoring services also offer a printout of statements providing a basic description of the most prominent aspects of the profile. A computerized system developed by the Section of Psychology at Mayo Clinic utilizes a a small deck of 23 standard computer data cards on which the MMPI items have been printed (Fig. 1). An electrographic pencil is used to mark the items. After completion, the deck is scored electronically and a computer printout is generated. The profile consists of two parts. The upper half of the form contains identifying information about the patient. The test scores for the various scales are also plotted to provide a visual representation of important factors. The bottom half of the printout contains a series of interpretive statements, selected according to certain rules, from more than 100 behavioral-descriptive phrases (Fig. 2). The library of statements contains no psychiatric terminology nor psychological jargon and provides a brief personality description of the patient. Beyond this information, the user is alerted to patients having a significant degree of mental-social-emotional distress by the phrase CONSIDER PSYCHIATRIC EVALUATION placed in a prominent position on the page. An MMPI response pattern suggesting a serious, but lesser, degree of distress would be identified to the clinician by the phrase MAY HAVE POOR SELF-CONCEPT; PROBABLY WOULD LIKE TO

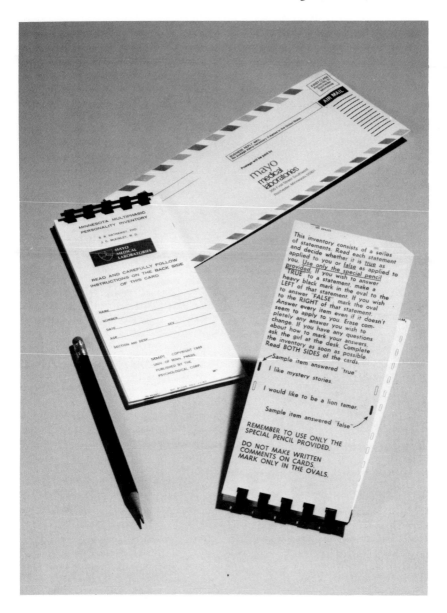

Fig. 1. Mayo Clinic MMPI decklet.

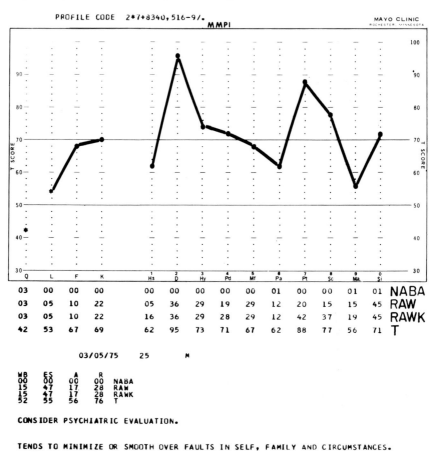

Fig. 2. Example of MMPI profile and Mayo Clinic computer printout.

DISCUSS EMOTIONAL PROBLEMS as the leading descriptive statement. Once alerted, the clinician may then wish to open a discussion of stresses felt by the client or may choose to refer the client to a mental health worker for further evaluation.

While the automated interpretation is self-explanatory, numerous references are available for the person who wishes to learn more about the MMPI (Pearson and Swenson, '67; Dahlstrom *et al.*, '72; Good and Brantner, '74; Graham, '77; Duckworth, '79).

MMPI Scales

Validity Scales. The Cannot Say Scale (Q) represents the total number of MMPI items that have not been answered by the patient or that have been marked both true and false. A high Q score may invalidate the whole inventory because of numerous unanswered items.

A high score on Scale L suggests an effort, usually conscious, to create a particular impression of being a very good person in the sense of having high moral, social, or ethical values.

The higher the score on Scale F, the greater is the likelihood that some factor has operated to invalidate the entire questionnaire. This may include lack of comprehension, poor reading ability, mental confusion, a deliberate desire to fake psychiatric illness, random marking of responses, or a machine scoring error.

Scale K measures a subtle level of psychological defensiveness. A moderate score indicates a view of the self as being well-adjusted, capable, and confident. A very high score on Scale K indicates an extreme degree of social and emotional well being, which is likely to be a denial of the true state of affairs.

Basic Clinical Scales. A high score on Scale 1 (Hs) suggests an undue concern with the state of one's body and preoccupation with possible symptoms of physical illness.

A high score on Scale 2 (D) indicates depression, sadness, pessimism, feelings of guilt, passivity, and a tendency to give up hope easily.

Scale 3 (Hy) represents a continuum of psychological maturity, with a high score characterizing people who are self-centered and superficial in their relationships with others and likely to utilize denial to a significant degree in dealing with psychological stress; they often have great difficulty gaining insight into their behavior.

A moderately high score on Scale 4 (Pd) describes assertiveness and nonconformity, while a very high score usually characterizes angry rebelliousness and a lack of identification with the usual social mores.

Scale 5 (Mf) provides an index of the range of interests held by the person. Males from higher socioeconomic backgrounds and those with advanced education often attain moderately high scores on this scale because of their varied interests. The scale is also sensitive to the person's view of the traditional male and female roles in our society and also seems to identify feelings of passivity, acquiescence, or dependency held by the person.

The scoring range on Scale 6 (Pa) measures interpersonal oversensitivity, irritability about the behavior or motives of others, and, finally, the suspicious thinking that often characterizes persons having a paranoid type of personality.

A high score on Scale 7 (Pt) indicates generalized feelings of anxiety and discomfort. There is often excessive rumination about personal inadequacies, whether real or imagined.

Scale 8 (Sc) represents an index of interpersonal discomfort. High scores are associated with feelings of detachment or alienation from the social realm extending to frank mental confusion and interpersonal aversiveness.

Scale 9 (Ma) assesses the level of psychological energy, with a high score characterizing talkativeness, distractability, physical restlessness, and, at times, impatience, irritability, or rapid mood swings.

A high score on Scale 0 (Si) indicates social introversion and a lack of desire to be with others, while a low score indicates social extroversion and an ability to enjoy the company of others.

Experimental Scales. The Ego Strength (Es) Scale provides a measure of resiliency of personality functioning and seems to reflect personal adaptability and internal resourcefulness. The Tired Housewife/Worried Breadwinner (Th/Wb) Scales are a particular set of age- and sex-related items that seem to reflect the kinds of psychological stresses experienced during the so-called midlife identity crisis. Scale A was developed from a factor analytic study of the MMPI and seems to represent general feelings of maladjustment or conscious anxiety. Scale R was developed during the same factor analytic study, with high scores characterizing psychological overcontrol of emotions and impulses.

Pilot Studies

While the MMPI is widely accepted and appears to be useful in a medical setting (Swenson *et al.*, '65; Swenson, '70; Osborne, '79), there are no reports in the literature regarding its specific use in evaluating patients who undergo orthognathic surgery. However, since 1975, we have accumulated some information that suggests the MMPI may also be helpful with this group of patients.

The MMPI profiles of 100 consecutive patients referred to the Mayo Clinic for orthognathic surgery (40 males, 60 females) revealed that a number of patients had significant psychological distress. Using the descriptive phrase from the computer printout CONSIDER PSYCHIATRIC REFERRAL as the criterion for severity, we found that 6 of the 40 males (15%) and 6 (10%) of the 60 females were affected. In addition, using the phrase from the printout MAY HAVE POOR SELF-CONCEPT; PROB-ABLY WOULD LIKE TO DISCUSS EMOTIONAL PROBLEMS as the criterion for a second level of emotional distress, we noted that six (15%) more males and seven (12%) more females were so identified. Thus, over-all, 25% of the sample expressed some psychological distress that would warrant further investigation.

In addition, a sample of twenty young patients (13 females, 7 males; mean age 21 years) were evaluated using the MMPI before and after surgery (follow-up ranged from 2 to 4 years). We were particularly inter-ested in the pre- to post-operative score changes on Scale 2 (feelings of depression), Scale 6 (oversensitivity to people), Scale 7 (anxiety), Scale 8 (interpersonal discomfort), Scale 0 (social introversion), and Scale Es (resiliency of personality). All patients in the sample described the surgi-cal outcome as satisfactory. It was speculated that improved dentofacial form would enhance personality development and social functioning and reduce the stresses associated with these disfiguring characteristics. The sample is small, and thus the report is only a preliminary one. However, after research on interpersonal attractiveness was reported by others (see papers by Berscheid, Adams, and Graber in this volume), the data are encouraging, because 16 (80%) of the 20 patients showed improvement in personality functioning. Analysis of the MMPI scores on Scales, 2, 7, 8, Si, and Es revealed significantly fewer feelings of anxiety and dysphoria or depression after surgery, as well as significantly increased comfort and interest regarding social relationships and activities ($P<0.05$, one-tailed t test). Feelings of oversensitivity (Scale 6) also were significantly reduced for females ($P<0.05$, one-tailed t test), but no changes were noted for males. An increase in the score on Scale 5 (role orientation) for females was unexpected, but interesting, because it suggests more feelings of interpersonal assertiveness after treatment ($P<0.05$, one-tailed t test).

SUMMARY

With the advent of refined and coordinated surgical and orthodontic techniques, the amount and variety of orthognathic surgical treatment have increased significantly during the past several years. If the most effective care is to be provided, evaluation of psychological, as well as physiological, factors is needed. For the orthognathic surgical patient, assessment of and responsiveness to personality factors associated with dentofacial disfigurement appear to be particularly important based on the research literature in the general area of interpersonal attraction. The MMPI, an extensively researched, objective personality assessment ques-tionnaire which has received widespread use in medical settings, appears to be a good tool for assessing the personality of orthognathic surgical patients. In addition, results of a pilot study using the MMPI to measure pretreatment and post-treatment changes indicates a significant improvement in personality functioning after orthognathic intervention.

REFERENCES

Dahlstrom, W. G., G. S. Welsh and L. E. Dahlstrom. *An MMPI Handbook. Vol. 1: Clinical Interpretation.* University of Minnesota Press, Minneapolis, 1972.

Duckworth, J. C. *MMPI Interpretation Manual for Counselors and Clinicians.* 2nd Ed., Accelerated Development, Muncie, Indiana, 1979.

Gillis, R. E., Jr., W. M. Swenson and W. R. Laney. Psychological factors involved in maxillofacial prosthetics. J. Prosthet. Dent. *41*:183-188, 1979.

Good, P. K.-E. and J. P. Brantner. *A Practical Guide to the MMPI: An Introduction for Psychologists, Physicians, Social Workers, and Other Professionals.* University of Minnesota Press, Minneapolis, 1974.

Graham, J. R. *The MMPI: A Practical Guide.* Oxford University Press, New York, 1977.

Harper, D. C. and L. C. Richman. Personality profiles of physically impaired adolescents. J. Clin. Psychol. *34*:636-642, 1978.

MacGregor, F. C. Facial disfigurement and problems of employment: some social and cultural considerations In: *Facial Disfigurement: A Rehabilitative Problem.* United States Department of Health, Education and Welfare, Washington, D. C., pp. 123-133, 1966.

Osborne, D. Use of the MMPI with medical patients. In: *New Developments in the Use of the MMPI.* J. N. Butcher (ed.), University of Minnesota Press, Minneapolis, pp. 141-163, 1979.

Ouellette, P. L. Psychological ramifications of facial change in relation to orthodontic treatment and orthognathic surgery. J. Oral Surg. *36*:787-790, 1978.

Pearson, J. S. and W. M. Swenson. *A User's Guide to the Mayo Clinic Automated MMPI Program.* Psychological Corporation, New York, 1967.

Pilling, L. F. Psychiatric aspects of diagnosis and treatment. In: *Prosthodontic Diagnosis and Treatment.* W. R. Laney and J. A. Gibilisco (eds.), Lea & Febiger, Philadelphia (in press).

Richardson, S. A., N. Goodman, A. H. Hastorf and S. M. Dornbusch. Cultural uniformity in reaction to physical disabilities. Am. Sociol. Rev. *26*:241, 1961.

Swenson, W. M. Automated personality assessment in medical practice. Med. Clin. North Am. *54*:835-849, 1970.

Swenson, W. M., H. P. Rome, J. S. Pearson and T. L. Brannick. A totally automated psychological test: experience in a medical center. J. A. M. A. *191*:925-927, 1965.

THE PSYCHOLOGICAL EFFECTS OF SURGICAL TREATMENT OF FACIAL DEFORMITY

Ian R. Munro, M.A., M.B., B.Chir., F.R.C.S.(C)

Associate Professor of Surgery, University of Toronto
Consultant Plastic Surgeon
The Hospital for Sick Children and Sunnybrook Medical Centre

There are many sayings which, because they are trite, are not understood. In Toronto, we have had a unique opportunity to learn and understand the meaning of trite sayings about the face. Our craniofacial team has assessed more than 1,000 patients with facial abnormalities and operated on more than 500 of these. We have learned that, although it is trite, it is true that the face is a person's single most distinguishing physical characteristic; an anomaly of the face takes precedence over any other physical defect; a deformity of the face can never be covered. The World Health Organization has stated: "An anomaly should be regarded as requiring treatment if the disfigurement or functional effect is, or is likely to be, an obstacle to the patient's physical and emotional well-being." Although this statement initially appears to be so broad that it has no value, it does characterize the wide variety of psychosocial reactions that are seen with regard to the face. There is little correlation between the severity of a facial anomaly and the reaction to it.

Congenital tumors which cause severe facial deformities, while they are understood, are not readily accepted and may have disastrous psychosocial effects, both on patients and their families. Facial deformity due to trauma is more easily understood and accepted (Brown, '76) and will not be considered here.

Congenital facial deformities produce the greatest adverse psychosocial reaction. Historically, facial deformity has been associated with mental retardation. Hogarth's paintings of depravity, as well as those displaying the inmates of mental institutions, are notorious for portraying ugly, deformed faces. A person's character is judged initially from the face; hence, we have the "high foreheaded intelligent professor" while a low forehead and beetling eyebrows are associated with stupidity or criminality. To have a grotesque child born is a shocking experience for both the parent and the doctor. The initial reaction is that the child also must be retarded. This concept is centuries old, and even well-trained pediatri-

171

Table 1. Toronto craniofacial team

Plastic Surgeon	Audiologist	Social Worker
Neurosurgeon	Speech Pathologist	Geneticist
Neuro-ophthalmologist	Orthodontist	Anthropologist
Neuroradiologist	Dentist	Medical Illustrator
Anaesthesiologist	Psychologist	
Otolaryngologist	Psychiatrist	

cians are still automatically judging such children as being retarded and usually as being untreatable. However, radical advances in craniofacial surgery have enabled us to study the psychological effects of facial deformity at all ages and to assess what psychological changes might occur after correction of the deformity.

The assumption that facial deformity has an adverse psychosocial effect on a person is not made by everyone. Often, well-educated doctors assume that a person does not need treatment because "he lives up north in a small community and has no problems." In 1970, a team was gathered in Toronto to assess the effects of orbital hypertelorism upon twelve patients. This study showed that none of these patients were living normal lives.

The treatment of congenital facial deformity is not simple. It is probably the most complex type of surgery known. For this reason, a team of 16 different specialties has been developed in Toronto (Table 1). The team has many functions, and the specific importance of each member has been reported previously (Munro, '75). Each team member is concerned with data collection and diagnosis within his own specialty, and certain members are involved in designing the appropriate operation. All members become involved in assessing the effect of the deformity upon the patient, his parents and his peers. In particular, we have found that each team member must realize that the problems associated with these patients are never routine, and each team member must develop extra areas of expertise. The most important member of the team should not be a plastic surgeon, but a craniofacial surgeon, who can devote his entire practice to these patients. However, a surgeon should not become involved in craniofacial surgery unless he has enough patients to maintain the necessary expertise.

There are many alternative methods from which to choose when trying to assess the psychological effect of correcting facial deformity. Patients could be grouped according to age, social background, financial status, education level, intelligence, environment or whether they come from a small community or large town. In this paper, the type of surgery is used as the basis for assessment. This is an arbitrary choice, as none of the bases for assessment have yielded a common denominator in predicting psychological reactions. Even the quality of result is an unreliable basis for predicting psychological change. The simplest procedures will be discussed first. This will be followed by a discussion of more complex procedures.

THE LOWER FACE

Osteotomies of the lower maxilla and mandible were originally designed to correct malocclusion. The Toronto team feels that the emphasis should be placed on correcting the cosmetic deformity associated with the malocclusion. In the 1960's, Obwegeser started combining a variety of orthognathic procedures and developed several new operations to correct all types of malocclusion. When treatment is designed for a patient, the Toronto team works on the basis of the face first, then the occlusion. There are many ways in which a normal occlusion can be produced, but the simplest technique will not necessarily produce the ideal face; hence, surgery may become quite complex.

Lip Protrusion

Figure 1 shows a patient with an anterior cross-bite. This was corrected by setting back the anterior six teeth with an intra-oral Köle ('70) procedure. In addition, the protrusive lower lip was rolled inward. Figure 1C shows the change in this patient's facial appearance, which was accompanied by a stunning improvement in body image. This patient was not considered deformed before the surgery, and the surgery was not major.

Figure 2A shows a patient who requested treatment for her protrusive lips. This was partially due to a bimaxillary protrusion, which is a frequent trait among blacks. Treatment consisted of a Köle procedure with recession of the upper teeth produced by the Wassmund ('35) technique and simultaneous advancement of the chin and rolling in of the lips. Figure 2B shows the patient one year after surgery. In addition to improved physical appearance, she has changed occupations from secretary to fashion model.

Mandibular Prognathism

The problem of mandibular prognathism is widely recognized, and effective treatment has been available for many years. Obwegeser ('64) devised an operation for the repositioning of the jaw in any direction without creating external scars. Malocclusion due to a small lower jaw, the commonest type, can be treated using Obwegeser's intra-oral sagittal

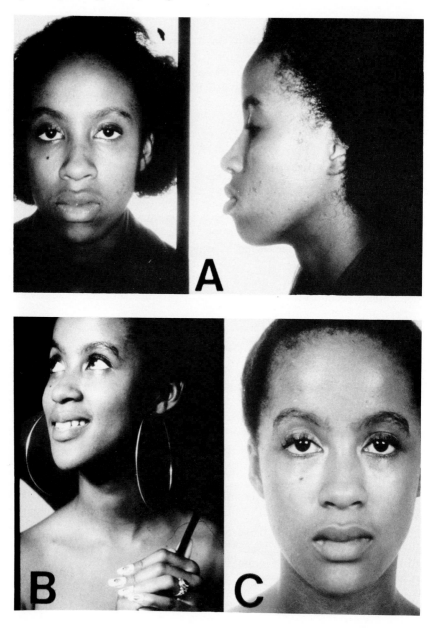

Figure 1. A sixteen-year-old girl with an anterior malocclusion and protrusive lower lip (A). Same patient three months after surgical correction (B) and one year after correction (C).

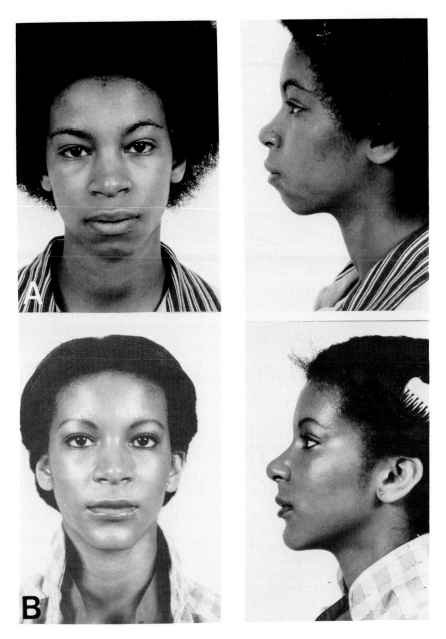

Figure 2. A. A twenty-three-year-old woman who requested correction of bimax-illary protrusion and thick lips. B. Same patient one year after surgical correction.

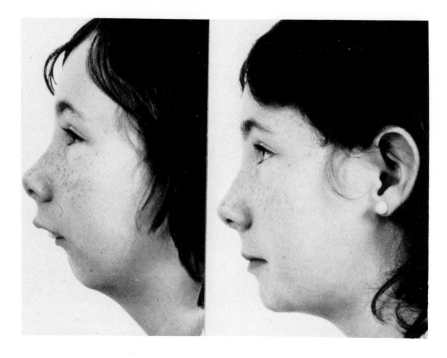

Figure 3. A fifteen-year-old girl with severe retrognathia (left). Same patient one year after intra-oral sagittal osteotomy was performed to advance the mandible (right).

splitting technique. The post-operative change in appearance is obvious (Fig. 3).

There is no age restriction for this surgery. Figure 4 shows a forty-year-old man before surgery (left) and one year after surgery (right). His change in self-image can be seen in the change in hairstyle and the carriage of his head, as well as in the fact that there was an improvement in his career.

Patients do not always reveal their true self-image prior to surgery, even to the psychosocial members of the team. Figure 5 shows a seventeen-year-old girl with a mild malocclusion before and one year after a complex intra-oral procedure. The girl was interviewed post-surgery on a television program and asked about her feelings regarding the surgery. Her response was not only enthusiastic, but she revealed that she had been called "chipmunk" before the surgery because of her chubby cheeks. She had not admitted to this before the surgery.

Not all patients respond with similar changes in self-image. Figure 6 shows a girl who is delighted with the dramatic improvement in her looks.

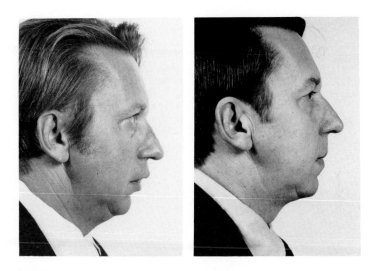

Figure 4. A forty-year-old male with a malocclusion and retrognathia (left). Same patient one year after correction (right).

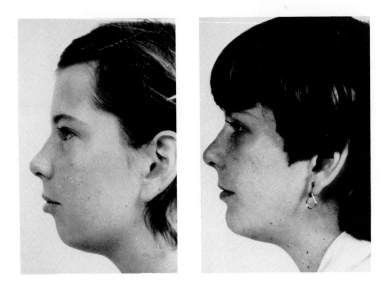

Figure 5. A sixteen-year-old girl with a malocclusion (left). The same patient one year after multiple simultaneous intra-oral procedures were performed to correct occlusion and produce a normal face (right).

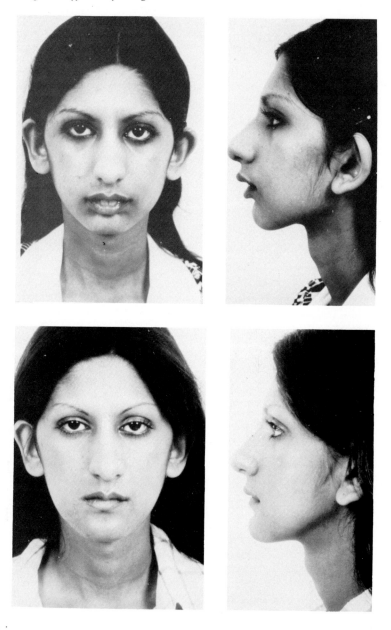

Figure 6. A sixteen-year-old girl with a malocclusion (top). Same patient two years after multiple simultaneous intra-oral procedures were performed to correct the occlusion and produce a normal face (bottom). Patient did not want to undergo further surgery for correction of protuberant ears.

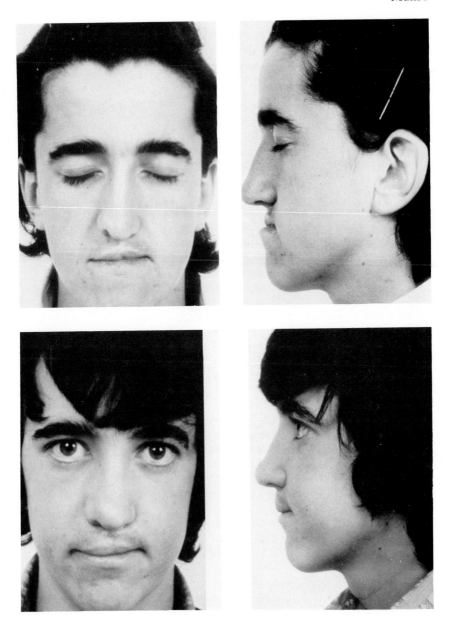

Figure 7. A seventeen-year-old boy with a malocclusion secondary to a cleft lip and palate (top). Same patient one year after a Le Fort I lower maxillary advancement (bottom).

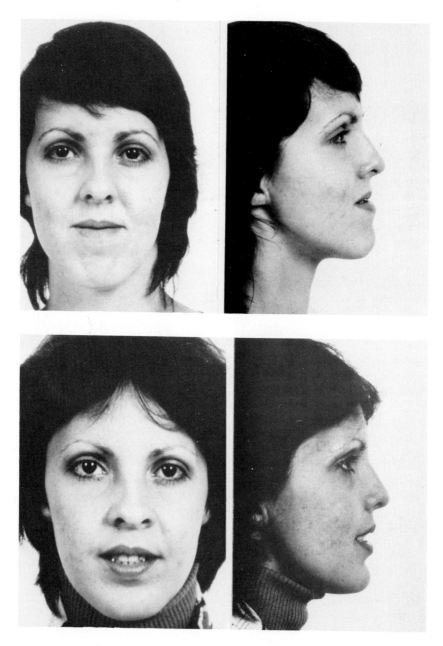

Figure 8. A twenty-year-old woman with mandibular prognathism and underdevelopment of the maxilla (top). Same patient two years after simultaneous intra-oral setback of the mandible and Le Fort I lower maxillary advancement (bottom).

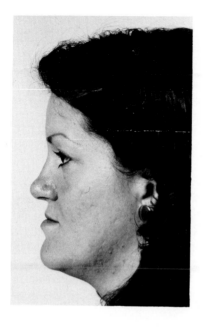 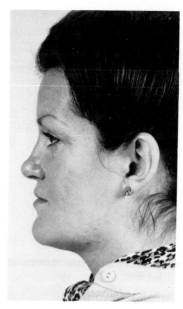

Figure 9. A thirty-three-year-old singer with the same deformity as patient seen in Figure 8 (left). Same patient one year after surgery was performed (right).

However, her appearance is still marred by outstanding ears, and she has remained adamant in resisting correction.

Cleft Lip/Palate

People who have a cleft lip and palate suffer from malocclusion due to retarded growth of the upper jaw. This can be corrected by a Le Fort I lower maxillary advancement osteotomy. Figure 7 shows a patient before and one year after such a procedure was performed. This boy's father, skeptical about the need for surgery, commented after surgery that he was now having to buy large quantities of meat for his son, who had been unable to eat steak before the surgery because of his malocclusion.

Maxillo-Mandibular Surgery

When planning correction, the team plans to produce a normal face and not just a normal occlusion. The patient in Figure 8 had mandibular prognathism and some flatness of the midface, Movement of either jaw would have corrected the occlusion but would not have produced the ideal facial balance achieved by moving both jaws. Figure 9 shows a patient before and after a similar jaw-switch procedure in whom the result was not as ideal as that seen for the patient in Figure 8. In addition, this patient was a singer who felt that her career was marred by her appearance. Post-operatively, her career did radically change for the better, as did her self-image and expectations. This woman had suffered severe burns to her chest as a child; her breasts were covered by skin grafts and scars, and she had no nipples. As a result of the facial change, she became more self-conscious of this and went on to have further surgery to her breasts, including the construction of nipples.

Binder's Syndrome

We have advocated the regionalization of craniofacial surgery, and this enables the recognition of new syndromes. Figure 10 shows patients that have the typical appearance of Binder's syndrome (maxillonasal dysplasia, Munro *et al.*, '79). Typically, they have a small flat nose. The anterior nasal spine is absent, and the central maxilla is underdeveloped, causing a Class III malocclusion. When these children were small, they were teased at school and called "flat-nose". For these people, rib and cartilage can be inserted along the nose and around the piriform margin to build out the lip. This is done as soon as there are psychological problems evident, even as young as age five years (Fig. 11).

Failure to recognize that a face is abnormal can lead to incorrect psychological treatment. The patient seen in Figure 12 was being treated, together with his parents, in a psychiatric unit for sociological breakdown. When our team psychiatrist saw this boy, he was immediately told that he had Binder's syndrome and that it could be corrected. The boy's facial expression changed immediately, as did his behavior. The parents did not react quite so positively until after correction.

Although failure to recognize a syndrome should not be condoned, it is sometimes more difficult to recognize when it is not accompanied by psychosocial maladjustment. The boy in Figure 13 was referred for treatment of his malocclusion. He was an average student with no severe psychosocial maladjustment. However, he was diagnosed as having Binder's syndrome and was treated by a Le Fort II osteotomy to move his nose and maxilla forwards. One year later he was gaining top marks at school and was participating in numerous sports. He became a team leader and also took up acting.

THE UPPER FACE

Crouzon's Syndrome

Modern major craniofacial surgery was first performed by Gilles (Gilles and Harrison, '50) in 1948 when he advanced the face of a patient with

Crouzon's syndrome. However, he felt the operation was so difficult that it should not be repeated. In the 1950's Tessier modified the procedure of the Le Fort III osteotomy, making it simpler (Tessier, '67).

Patients with Crouzon's syndrome tend to be of above average intelligence. With the help of good parents, they can manage reasonably well. The boy seen in Figure 14 was a good student with just two good friends. He had managed to develop an acting career of which he was proud. He was curious about what would happen to his career if he had his face changed. Because this surgery carries such great technical risks, it is dangerous to predict for a patient what the result might be. However, as a result of surgery, his career did change, and no longer did he play the role of the buffoon or village idiot but gained lead roles as the good-looking hero.

In some patients who have Crouzon's or Apert's syndrome, the airway may be obstructed due to retromaxillism. One girl spent the first 14 years of her life sleeping in her parents' bedroom so that they could listen for any airway problems. After this problem was corrected, she went on to become a nurse. When she became engaged she and her fiance presented a different problem to the craniofacial team when they came in for genetic counselling. They were told that Crouzon's is an autosomal dominant condition with a 50% chance of inheritance. They also were told that patients with Crouzon's syndrome now are being effectively treated in infancy. She replied that she would produce at least four children.

The adolescent patient seen in Figure 15 was described as having the "face of a criminal" and was referred for treatment in the hope of correcting his antisocial behavior. After surgical correction, the boy's behavior did change. He took a job and later went to university. He developed enough insight to be able to explain that his previous behavior had been due to other people's reaction to his face.

Quantitative analysis of the face has resulted in improvements in craniofacial surgery. In the profile of an ideal face, the eyebrow is normally 15-20 mm in front of the cornea, and the skin over the inferior orbital rim is level with the cornea. To provide ideal facial correction, it is necessary to advance the forehead as well as the middle face. In severe skeletal underdevelopment, the eye is anterior to the orbital rim (exorbitism) and is at risk of blindness either from direct trauma or from prolapse of the eye through the eyelids, with entrapment behind. The boy seen in Figure 16 is blind in his left eye from such a prolapse. He labelled his pre-operative self-image drawing, which he did for the team psychiatrist, "frog-face". The nickname is very common for patients with Crouzon's syndrome. One year post-operatively, he labelled his drawing as "the six-million-dollar man".

The improvement of genetic facial deformities via surgical correction

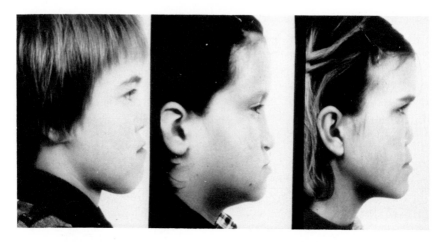

Figure 10. Three unrelated boys with Binder's syndrome.

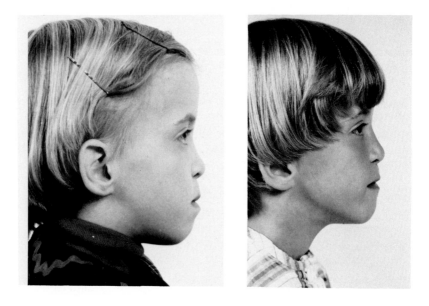

Figure 11. A five-year-old girl with Binder's syndrome who had been teased about her small nose (left). Same patient one year after a cartilage graft had been added along the dorsum and around the base of her nose (right).

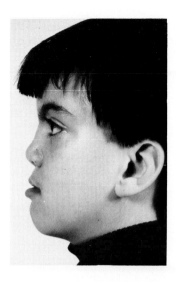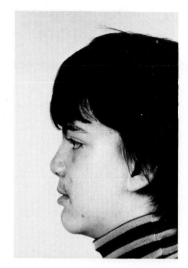

Figure 12. A twelve-year-old boy with Binder's syndrome (left). Same patient one year after advancement of his nose and upper jaw (right).

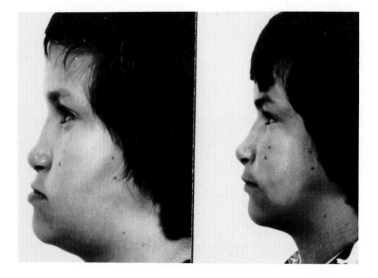

Figure 13. A fourteen-year-old boy with Binder's syndrome (left). Same patient one year after advancement and lengthening of his nose and advancement of his upper jaw (right).

185

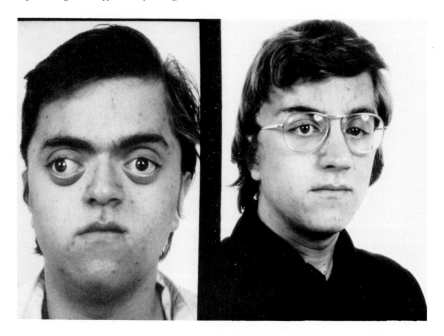

Figure 14. A seventeen-year-old boy with Crouzon's syndrome (left). Same patient two years after surgical correction (right).

may also yield unexpected consequences, sometimes related to the family environment. This was first realized after the surgical correction of a child with Crouzon's syndrome who had complained prior to surgery that he did not like the taste of his mother's food. As a result of moving his face and forehead forward, he developed the sense of smell, which had been absent due to the obstructed nasal airway. Because he could smell, the food no longer tasted bland. He returned one year after surgery forty pounds heavier and looking exactly like his mother both in body habitus and facial features.

Apert's Syndrome

Apert's syndrome has facial features similar to Crouzon's, but also has syndactyly (fusion) of the web of all the fingers and toes. Traditionally, these patients have been labelled mentally retarded. Some *are* retarded, but this is secondary to untreated hydrocephalus and craniostenosis. Current treatment of these children in the first few months of life consists of treating the hydrocephalus, releasing the craniostenosis and advancing the forehead. Since this treatment plan has been initiated, the craniofacial team has seen no Apert's child who was not capable of being educated at

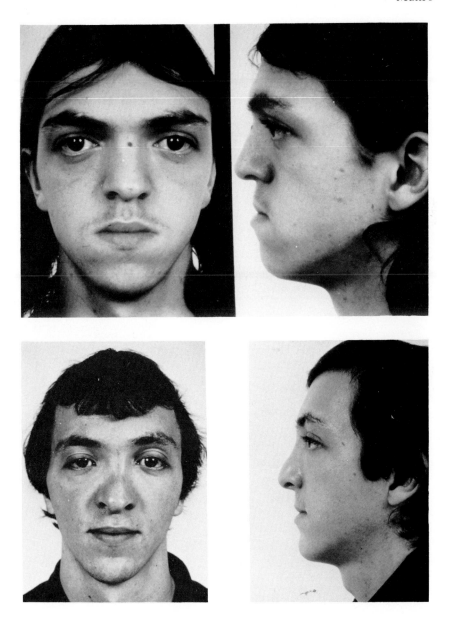

Figure 15. A sixteen-year-old boy with Crouzon's syndrome (top). Note the over-hang of superior orbital ridges, the widespaced eyes (orbital hypertelorism), and the underdevelopment of the midface and receding chin. The same patient two years after a one-step correction of all the anomalies (bottom).

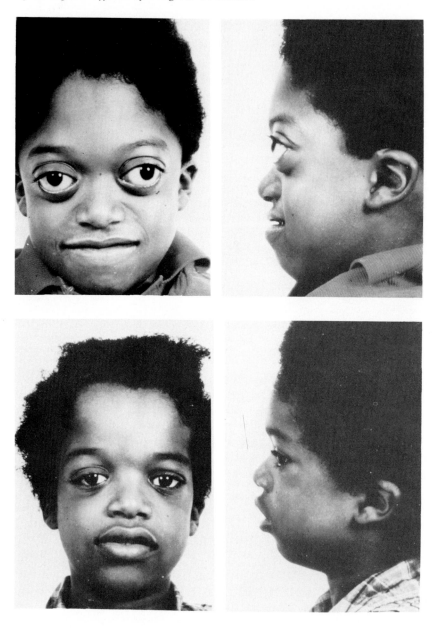

Figure 16. A six-year-old boy with Crouzon's syndrome who is blind in his left eye from exorbitism (top). Same patient one year after advancement of forehead and midface was performed to protect his eyes (bottom). In addition to protecting the eyes, the surgery produced a normal occlusion and profile.

school. Unfortunately, many of these patients are placed in institutions for the mentally retarded in infancy purely because of their appearance. We have one child who was in such an institution until, at age 10, it was realized she was normal. Her face was corrected at age 15, and at age 21 she was attending university, learning to become a social worker to help mentally retarded people.

Orbital Hypertelorism

The most dramatic development in craniofacial surgery was Tessier's development of the technique for the correction of orbital hypertelorism by moving the eyes and orbits closer together. This has produced a tremendous opportunity for studying the psychological changes that occur when a deformity is corrected. The patient seen in Figure 17 had the same facial expression in infancy that she had prior to surgery at age 17. Three months after surgery, she had changed her style of dress and was more socially active, although her face was far from ideal. She went on to train as a nursing assistant.

Not all patients react adversely to severe deformity. The boy in Figure 18 attended a normal school and had several friends prior to correction at age 9. Ideally, the correction of orbital hypertelorism should be done in infancy, enabling a child to grow without the stress of disfigurement (Fig. 19). However, this may cause a professionally difficult situation because, if the results are good, the parents may be prepared to take the risk of producing another deformed child.

The results of this kind of surgery are not always good, but merely having something done is sometimes enough to change a person. The patient in Figure 20 was a recluse. As a child, she had been hidden by her parents. Whenever guests came to the house, she was told to go to her room until they left. When she and her family went on picnics to the countryside, she was made to stay in the car, rather than frighten other people. By the time she was thirty-three, she would never leave her house. After surgery and still with some residual facial defects (Fig. 20D), she became involved in community projects and traveled long distances on public transport with aplomb.

Not all severely deformed people are treated so adversely by their parents and may grow up in a sheltered environment only to have the true horror of their predicament revealed when they leave this protection. The girl in Figure 21 was brought up on a farm. When she moved to a large city and found everyone staring at her and was unable to get a job, she was devasted. The surgical procedure for correcting orbital hypertelorism carries four main risks—death, brain damage, blindness and infection. These risks are always enumerated to the patient or parents. This

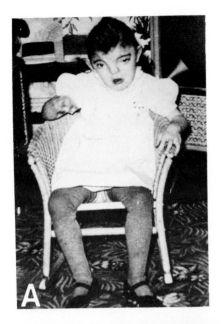

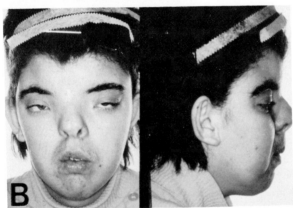

Figure 17. A. An eighteen-month-old girl with the wide-spaced eyes of orbital hypertelorism. B. Same patient at age 17 years. C. Same patient three months after surgical repositioning of the eyes and orbits.

190

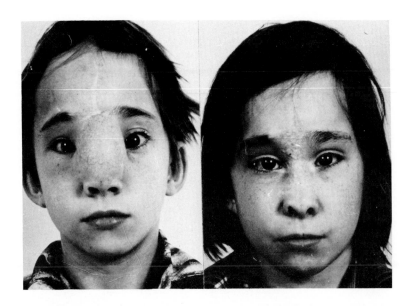

Figure 18. A nine-year-old boy with orbital hypertelorism and frontal encephalo-cele (left). Same patient one year after surgical correction (right).

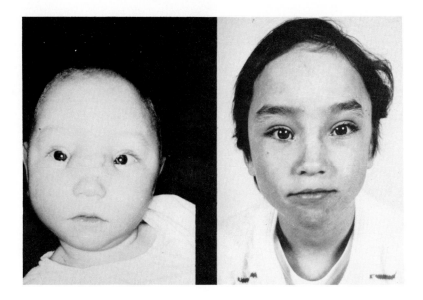

Figure 19. A ten-month-old boy with orbital hypertelorism and frontal encephalo-cele (left). Same patient eight years after correction (right).

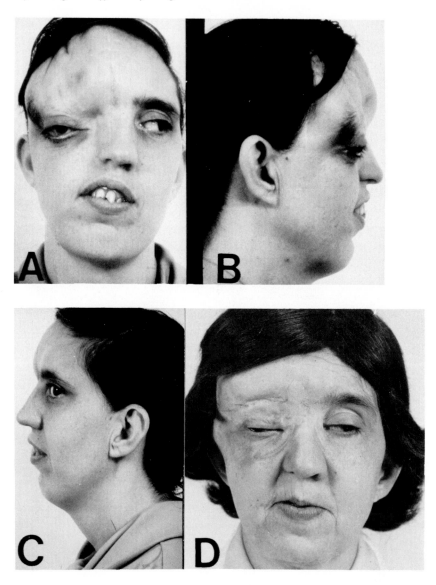

Figure 20. A thirty-three-year-old woman with severe orbital hypertelorism and facial asymmetry (A-C). D. Same patient one year after a two-stage correction.

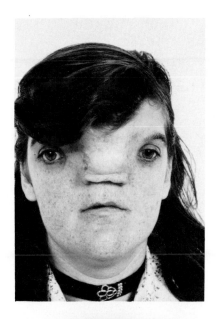

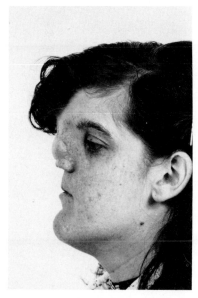

Figure 21. A twenty-five-year-old woman with nasal encephalocele and severe orbital hypertelorism (inter-canthal distance 75 mm; top). Same patient eighteen months after correction (bottom).

girl said she would be better dead than trying to live as she was. Subsequent to correction, she got a job. The initial change was dramatic, but further improvement could have been achieved around the eyes. However, this girl was so pleased that she refused further help. This is a problem seen frequently by the craniofacial team.

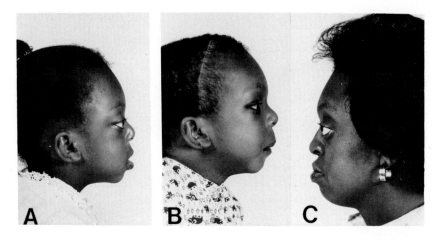

Figure 22. A. A four-year-old girl with Crouzon's syndrome and exorbitism. B. Same patient two months after advancement of forehead and maxilla. C. Patient's mother with untreated Crouzon's syndrome.

Sometimes successful treatment of a deformity for one person may stimulate introspection that was previously absent in another person. The child in Figure 22A was referred because of the risk to her eyesight from exorbitism. After correction (Fig. 22B), the mother (Fig. 22C) promptly asked if it would be possible for her to be treated.

The birth of a severely deformed child can be so stressful that a family splits apart. However, the stress surrounding major surgery can bring a family closer together. This is even more likely if there are medical complications.

PSYCHOLOGICAL EFFECTS OF ADVANCES IN CRANIOFACIAL SURGERY

The techniques of craniofacial surgery have advanced so much that extensive tumors around the orbit can now be treated in one operation. It has been demonstrated that it is more stressful to have a congenital tumor than to acquire one later in life. It has also been shown that a positive response to surgery is much greater for the former than for the latter.

The boy in Figure 23 had never been outside the home environment. This was not because the parents rejected him, but because they realized that the public could not accept him. In one radical procedure, half the face was removed and the skeleton was repositioned. Although he is no longer grotesque, the parents have greater difficulty adjusting to the fact

194

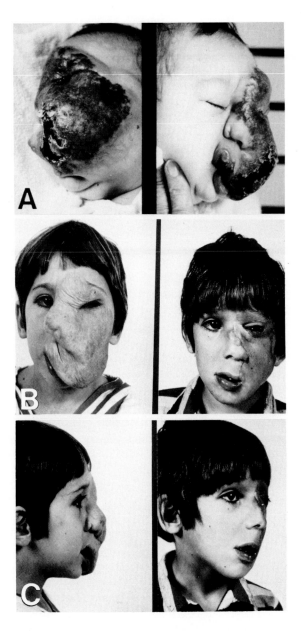

Figure 23. A. Three-month-old boy with giant haemangioma. B. Same patient at age five years. There is massive overgrowth of underlying bone, as well as soft tissue overgrowth. C. Patient six months after excision of the entire tumor and repositioning of the skeleton. More procedures will be performed.

that their child could now go out into public than did the child, himself. Indeed, six months after surgery, while waiting in an airport, the child noticed a woman staring at him. He went over to her and said, "You should have seen what I used to look like."

The 18-year-old boy in Figure 24 has neurofibromatosis. He had never been to school and was illiterate. Eighteen months after surgery he could read and write and simultaneously was going to school and being trained for a job. The patient in Figure 25 has fibrous dysplasia, which is not congenital but of slow onset, causing progressive facial distortion with orbital displacement. Surgery consisted of total removal of all involved bone and rebuilding the skull and orbit with rib grafts. This patient, and others like her, did not develop a warped psyche before the surgery and consequently, although pleased by the results of surgery, did not undergo a dramatic personality change after surgery.

Research

There has been little research done on the psychosocial effects of major craniofacial surgery. A preliminary study of seventy patients by the craniofacial team psychiatrist (Lefebvre and Munro, '78) found that the patients rated themselves as less deformed than did the parents or surgeon and that girls rated themselves as more deformed than did the boys. However, there was a close correlation in the deformity rating between that of the parents and that of the team members. Post-operative satisfaction with the surgery at one year was generally very high. Dissatisfaction was related either to unrealistic expectations for perfect features or to parents who were still in a denial phase and felt they had been pushed into surgery against their better judgment. It should be noted here that it is imperative that the patient be fully informed of the risks of surgery and the anticipated amount of improvement.

CONCLUSIONS

The children seen by the craniofacial team became aware of their facial anomaly at a very early age due to the reaction of parents, siblings and strangers toward them. Strong parental support helped these children to accept their deformity, but each change of environment, such as meeting strangers or changing schools, threw a renewed stress upon them. Although they often learned to protect themselves, self-image drawings revealed that they were fully aware of their deformity. Maximum stress occurred when the patients left their protected home environment in order to go to school or to work. Intelligence and other physical attributes helped to provide a positive self-image. The severity of the psycho-

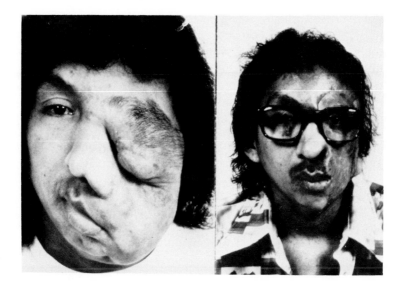

Figure 24. An eighteen-year-old boy with giant neurofibromatosis (left). Same patient two years after excision of entire left side of his face and reconstruction of bone anomalies (right).

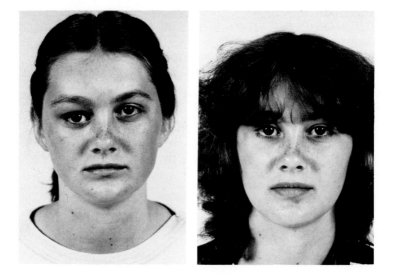

Figure 25. A sixteen-year-old girl with right orbital dystopia and forehead prominence from fibrous dysplasia (left). Patient one year after excision of forehead and orbit and reconstruction with rib grafts (right).

social impairment did not seem to be directly related to the degree of deformity. Positive psychosocial changes began with the patient's first contact with the craniofacial team because the patient was no longer treated as a freak, but just as someone with a problem that needed to be corrected.

Post-operatively, the psychological changes could not be related to the type of deformity or to the degree of improvement. Our patients were reluctant to undergo multiple operations or "touch-up" procedures; hence, everything possible was done to produce correction in one stage. During the stage when the surgery was designed, plans were made to produce the maximum correction, regardless of the complexity of the surgery that was needed.

Very positive psychological changes occurred after surgery at all ages. Patients and parents very quickly forgot the severity of the pre-operative situation, and it was necessary to remind them sometimes by photograph. Patient satisfaction was usually much higher than that of the parents or the team. However, it is essential that the craniofacial team remain the most dissatisfied group if they are to constantly strive for improvement in results. The performance of major types of craniofacial surgery is difficult and dangerous and should be done only by a few specialized centers to safeguard the patients and allow the development of enough experience to permit the conception of new ideas (Tessier, '71; Munro, '73).

Experience so far reveals that it is better for the patient and parents to have the surgery performed at the youngest age possible. Even if subsequent growth distorts an initially good result, surgery can always be repeated, and the child is not condemned to a prolonged period of living with a facial anomaly. Furthermore, if the patient and parent have once seen a good correction, they are far more prepared to wait until the appropriate time for a second surgical procedure, should they see growth causing distortion.

ACKNOWLEDGMENTS

The author has much pleasure in thanking the members of the Toronto Hospital for Sick Children Craniofacial Team for the continued support and treatment of these patients; in particular, Dr. A. Lefebvre, psychiatrist, and Ms. S. Barclay, social worker, for their input and Ms. Adrienne Pancer for typing and proof-reading this manuscript.

REFERENCES

Brown, T.E. Ego in distress. Chapter X. In: *Rehabilitation of the Facially Disfigured.* C.C. Thomas, Springfield, Illinois, 1973.

Gilles, H. and S.H. Harrison. Operative correction by osteotomy of recessed malar maxillary compound in a case of oxycephaly. Br. J. Plast. Surg. *3*:123, 1950.

Lefebvre, A. and I.R. Munro. The role of psychiatry in a craniofacial team. Plast. Reconstr. Surg. *61*(4):564, 1978.

Munro, I.R. Orbito-cranio-facial surgery: the team approach. Plast. Reconstr. Surg. *55*:170, 1975.

Munro, I.R., W.J. Sinclair and N.L. Rudd. Maxillonasal dysplasia (Binder's syndrome). Plast. Reconstr. Surg. *63*(5):657, 1979.

Obwegeser, H. L. The indications for surgical correction of mandibular deformity by the sagittal splitting technique. Br. J. Oral Surg. *1*:157, 1964.

Reichenback, E., H. Köle and H. Brückl. *Chirurgische Kieferorthopädie*. J. A. Barth Verlagsbuchhandlung, Leipzig, 1970.

Tessier, P. Osteotomies totales de la face. Syndrome de Crouzon. Syndromed-Apert. Oxycephalies. Scaphocephalies. Turricephalies. Ann. Chir. Plast. *12*:273, 1967.

Tessier, P. The scope and principles: dangers and limitations and the need for special training in orbitocranial surgery. In: *Transactions of the Fifth International Congress of Plastic and Reconstructive Surgery*. Butterworth, Melbourne, Australia. 1971.

Wassmund, M. *Lehrbuch der Praktischen Chirurgie des Mundes und der Kiefer, Bd. 1.* J. A. Barth Verlagsbuchhandlung, Leipzig, 1935.

SURGERY, ACTIVISM AND AESTHETICS: A SOCIOLOGICAL PERSPECTIVE ON TREATING FACIAL DISFIGUREMENT

Ronald P. Strauss, D.M.D., Ph.D.

Associate Professor of Dentistry and Dental Director
Oral, Facial and Communicative Disorders Program
University of North Carolina

INTRODUCTION

There are common elements in how societies relate to disfiguration, but each brings its special fears, myths and explanations into the formulation of an appropriate response. This paper will examine how a society responds to physical deviation and how culture and world-view affect this response. In particular, it will clarify how modern medicine deals with disfigurement and will evaluate the impact that this medical intervention has on social life. The medical response, in our society, is the result of a rational and scientific framework. This is not the only response possible, and this paper will discuss how this selection implies that certain moral and ethical choices are being made.

Pre-scientific man believed and acted as though the occurrence of events could be altered and determined through spiritual action. Priests and shamans provided explanations for events, and people were able to intercede in the course of fate through their spiritual and psychic powers. The advent of science served to discredit the view that the spiritual and sacred are the prime elements in understanding the world and reality. Science provided an alternative explanation in which the systematic pursuit of knowledge became the means by which truths and laws were determined. The rational perspective means that reason and calculation are the basis of establishing truth. In order to accomplish a desired practical aim, technology and technical knowledge are employed. The growth of science and technology since the Industrial Revolution resulted in an increase in the ability to control the human physical environment. The presumed freedom to act independently of ultimate mysteries or gods is the embodiment of secular principles and the origin of Western activism. This activism has meant that man feels able to intervene in human problems through the exercise of technical skill. Western medicine is a crystallization of this secular perspective and acts to control human suffering in a powerful manner.

Science, technology and medicine have proven capable of altering the conditions of life to the extent that a great deal of trust, expectation and mythology have emerged. Indeed, since physicians can influence birth, life and death, they are believed to be deserving of autonomy and trust. As a consequence of this deference, cultural stereotypes of physicians have developed. The stereotype that most clearly embodies medical activism is that of the surgeon. The heroic and noble image of the surgeon has created absurd stereotypes that nevertheless convey power. The stereotypic surgeon, always a male, takes on death and disease with his hands and his knife; he is an exorcist who cuts out that which is ill and restores people to normal functioning. The imagery surrounding these secular gods thrives on the public's need to believe and the professionals' enjoyment of the status, power and roles they are granted. As with most standardized conceptions there are elements of truth here, yet the distortion is evident to all who become aware of the limitations of knowledge and the restrictions as to what a surgeon can actually do. The image of the surgeon as activist, as well as the practice of surgery itself, does appear to have appeal within American society. Particularly evident is the impact cosmetic surgery has had on aesthetic and social values in American life.

Cosmetic surgery has altered our perceptions of physical deviance. It has altered how physical beauty is used to establish social hierarchies and affected the understanding of what is normal. It has changed our tolerance for human differences and has raised questions regarding egalitarianism and the equity of the distribution of medical resources. Let us first examine different ways of responding to deformity and then evaluate the medical response.

PERCEPTIONS OF DEFORMITY

The range of cultural responses to deformity includes rejection, integration, discrimination, elimination, rehabilitation and preventive intervention. All cultures recognize human differences and have mechanisms to cope with deviance. The labels which are given to deviants in *this* society carry a connotation of devaluation. The cripple, the freak, the monster, the mutant, the lunatic, the moron and the queer are all marked as blemished individuals who must face social rejection. To define someone as handicapped places them in a discredited and discounted category which constrains their modes of interaction with normals. Goffman ('63) has discussed this in some detail and points out that: "The attitudes we normals have towards a person with a stigma

202

and the actions we take in regard to him . . . are what benevolent social action is designed to soften and ameliorate. . .we believe the person with a stigma is not quite human."

Segregation of individuals who are disfigured or otherwise stigmatized exists in many cultures. Cloistered settings such as leper colonies, mental institutions or other asylums function to keep deviance hidden and to protect the population of normals. The numbers of persons who have been placed in institutions because of physical and mental disabilities is a measure of tolerance within a society. In a variety of societies, the physician or healer serves as the gatekeeper (Fox and Swazey, '74) for entrance to institutions and thereby controls the public visibility of disabilities.

Genocide and infanticide are the extremes in social control of physical deformity. In Nazi Germany, the handicapped, insane and deformed were included in the death camps along with Jews, Gypsies and homosexuals. The notion of a pure master race left little room for differences. Evidently, mass killings began in 1939 with euthanasia or mercy killings of the insane or those with "useless lives" (Ivy, '47). Sterilization and castration experiments were performed in order to discover a way to control reproduction. Eugenics was also employed as a means of deviance control.

Gustafson ('73) states, "The growing capacities for intervention in the course of development of human life raise, in an exacerbated form, one of the oldest of philosophical and theological questions, namely, what is the normatively human?" Innovations such as amniocentesis, *in vitro* fertilization and recombinant DNA research have focused concern on whether genetic controls can be used to reduce variation and limit human deformity and deviance. Abortion and infant euthanasia can be used to terminate the lives of grossly defective human beings. It is interesting to consider that amniocentesis and abortion provide a society with little more active ability to screen deviance and determine norms than did infanticide in ancient Greece. Davis ('70) discusses the possibility that fundamental research into prevention of mutations and malignant cellular changes might contribute to the possibility of gene transfer and cloning in humans. The prospect of cloning may involve the imposition of one conceptualization of "normal" on a whole population. While much more can be said regarding genetic engineering, it is clearly one potential way of dealing with deformity.

Some cultures have chosen to value and appreciate physical or mental deviance. Fiedler ('78) points to the French word *phenomenes* which is used to avoid negativity or condescension in labeling *very special people*. Many religions and cultures consider deformity as a sign of grace and spiritual power or vengeance. Fascination with disfigurement, particularly in a mythical sense, is found in literary fantasy (e.g., *Gulliver's Travels*,

The Hunchback of Notre Dame) and in the continuing appeal of monster movies and freak shows.

The positive, or at least interested, perception of deformity may be a factor in encouraging the integration of deformed individuals into a society. Most societies have—within limits—attempted the inclusion of deviant individuals into community life. This implies the ability to accept such individuals into a legitimate social role. The village idiot and the fool were tolerated and functioned within a defined identity. In many developing countries, a role for the openly disfigured individual exists, particularly since medical services are still focused on survival needs rather than on the need for correcting deformities. It is not unusual to see people with unrepaired cleft lips or clubbed feet on the streets or in the marketplaces of many locales. The range of openly displayed disfigurement varies even within the developed Western nations. The impact of the World Wars on European life has meant that amputees and other disabled persons are quite visually evident. The willingness to "see" deviance implies at least some empathy and flexibility in dealing with such individuals.

In the United States, changes in the social status of the handicapped are somewhat evident and are largely out-growths of the civil rights and consumer movements. Alterations in terminology (exceptional instead of handicapped classes), increases in physical access (barrier-free design) and antidiscrimination legislation (equal opportunity) are responses to interest groups that have formed to protect the rights of this minority. Movements towards deinstitutionalization and mainstreaming are directed towards increasing the integration of deviants into community life and creating a more tolerant social environment. Measures such as these historically fit into an egalitarian ethic in American life that seeks to preserve equality of opportunity. As in the case of other minority groups, social integration depends on economic costs. The high cost of rehabilitation and renovation of facilities may become a serious limitation.

Social hierarchies can form to deal with human differences within a culture. Social hierarchies create a condition wherein people can reassure themselves of their acceptability and understand their place within the power and status relations of the group. Being part of the in-crowd guarantees security and order as well as satisfying the need to belong, to share and to know one's place. Particularly in a child's world of fears, being different is frightening because it means not sharing with the larger group and results in isolation. Rules against being different create order as well as encourage conformity. The formation of the basically homogeneous in-crowd depends upon the existence of outsiders—of rejects or deviants. Indeed, the cohesion of many social movements depends on the normals believing themselves to better than the people they define as deviant. The Nazis had Jews to remind them of their superiority as the master race; whites in South Africa have the blacks; the hardhats have the hippies. Physical characteristics provide an easy and reliable means to define group membership since they are readily evident. When visible characteristics do not occur naturally (e.g., skin color), groups develop signs to represent affiliation. The Nazis used arm bands to distinguish Jews in this way. Outcasts sometimes find group cohesion in the fact that they share an identity—being different. When the Black Power movement developed, symbols of membership such as afro haircuts and clenched fists emerged. These symbols identified individuals who desired affiliation and who actively attempted to redefine power relations so that the dominant society was not perceived as desirable. Typically, the dominant social groups develop myths and fantasies about the deviant, thereby giving some power and mystery to being different. Distortions and fantasies fuel already present discrimination and may also be an outlet for the fear that one may in actuality be, or become, deviant. In the case of a disfigured person, the threat to normals is especially potent since no one can be absolutely immune to acquired deformities. Perhaps it is the universality of the threat of becoming disfigured or giving birth to a deformed child that makes us so interested in being able to remedy or alter members of this group.

This discussion of perceptions of deformity and social controls has shown the variety and range of possible responses. The question that next occurs is, what are the ramifications of selecting medicine and the physician to be the dominant societal response?

MEDICAL TREATMENT AND AESTHETIC NORMS

American society has chosen to deal with deformity as illness in a medical context. Medicine has responded by attempting to alter the physical characteristics of deformed persons, thereby covering up or repairing differences. Cosmetic plastic surgery has been a particularly effective means of correcting disfigurements. There is little question that plastic surgery has been used as a tool to control human differences. MacGregor ('74) discusses plastic surgery eloquently, pointing out how rhinoplasty procedures (nose-jobs) were used to alter ethnic characteristics in cultural groups (particularly Jews) wishing to integrate themselves into American society. In a similar way, such surgery has permitted the correction of physical deviations to normal. The process of normalization of physical appearance raises several serious questions that focus on cultural definitions of what is normal, what is deformed and what is acceptable. What should the appropriate response to deformity be? Should this be a concern of medicine? Should society integrate a broader range of physical features into its definition of normal? What does it mean to allow medicine the right to make these distinctions? When a surgeon fixes a face, to what standard of beauty does he refer?

These questions take on special importance when the face is the part of the body under consideration. The face cannot easily be hidden and is especially significant in social interaction. The face is central to both verbal and non-verbal communication, receiving great attention as a means of understanding motives, responses and personality. First impressions, the medium for rapid interpersonal evaluation and choice, are largely based upon physical attraction. A marked face may misguide perceptions by covering the actual identity of the individual. Psychological research has revealed the significance of appearance and attractiveness in the socialization process. There is little doubt that peer acceptance, friendship, sex and mating are particularly responsive to physical cues. It should be clear that this essay does not call the importance of appearance into question but wishes to examine the criteria for its alteration.

Standards of beauty vary greatly from culture to culture, yet all standards have some characteristics in common. Physical attractiveness can be thought of as a phenomenon that has a population distribution. Let us construct a hypothetical social experiment in which a representative sample of people drawn from a single cultural group are asked to rate the facial appearance of a representative sample of members of that group on a 7 point scale. The scale and the hypothesized results of the experiment are seen in Figure 1. The bell-shaped curve distribution has a slight skew towards attractive, since that which is seen as attractive is also that to which we are, at least, accustomed. The unusual or exceptional faces are relegated places at both extremes of the distribution categories and contain few members. While the criteria should vary from culture to culture, the distribution should remain approximately the same. Even within a culture, standards of beauty change from era to era.

To take this hypothetical experiment one step further, the hypothetical subjects are asked to select a place on the continuum where facial appearance becomes unacceptable and then examine what the options are for these persons. In ancient Greece, infanticide might be the lot for children with unacceptable appearance. A similar fate might occur in some indigenous groups in modern times as well. In American culture, prior to cosmetic surgery, the unacceptably ugly or deformed person was stigmatized and hidden, although this fate was probably reserved for a very small percentage of people (those that were at the very end of the distribution). The range of generally normal and acceptable was probably broad, since it was costly to exclude large numbers of a society from social functioning.

The advent of facial plastic surgery opened the possibility of remediation to those in the visually unacceptable range and, therefore, permitted more people to be placed or to place themselves in the unacceptable categories. Labelling a broader number of people as unacceptable becomes possible only when the prospect of remediation exists which makes it possible to return many to acceptable status. Technological and surgical changes may stimulate an increase in the numbers of persons defined as deviant, especially children. The range of normality, especially in childhood (prior to repair), is smaller than it once was, and I would suggest that the possibility of remedying a condition permits that condition to be considered unacceptable. A good example of this is the Class II malocclusion (relative maxillary protrusion). It seems plausible that a child who may have been acceptably buck-toothed in the 1940's, and who may have been a candidate for orthodontic braces in the 1950's and early 1960's, now often has a dentofacial deformity, the treatment for which is maxillofacial surgery. The expansion of medical attention directed towards this non-life-threatening condition serves to increase its unacceptability as normal. Indeed, what was once probably a minor variant of normal has become a deformity. Does the advent of new types of surgery reawaken concerns in people who had accepted their disfigurement and the social role that accompanies it? The more that can be done to alter differences, the less acceptable they become. One must ask the question: Who should control this process of definition and treatment elaboration?

SURGICAL VALUES AND CONTROLS ON TREATMENT

The criteria for beauty in American society is transmitted quite explicitly in movies, television and advertising. The physician does not create the standards but is one of several agents empowered to preserve them. In the process of preserving standards, physicians encourage and support them. The time and resources spent on cosmetics in American society are immense and create a multibillion dollar per year industry (MacGregor, '74). We must consider that while the medical profession affects societal values, it is, in a very basic sense, a reflection of the larger society's values and needs. Critics of the medical profession sometimes place blame on that profession for what they consider to be excesses in medicine, without considering that doctors perform functions which society, in general, and their patients, in particular, desire of them.

Treatment of deformities or defects within a medical model defines the condition as illness and the person as a patient. This context is also an activist one in which the medical professional is expected to respond by "fixing up" the patient. Such a situation benefits the health-care marketplace by increasing demand for services. Medicine is conducted within an economic system that determines how it is practiced and how rewards are distributed, and there is little reason to believe that the medical professionals would act to alter a system that has rewarded them well. The decision to physically rehabilitate people is a response to several economic and social forces. These include: family and individual demand for services, the desire to prevent people from becoming unproductive or dependent on the social welfare system, financial gain to the provider, hospital or institution, and a mandate to protect the aesthetic standards of the culture. Cost/benefit analysis seeks to define what the payback from rehabilitation is, since it is not clear that workplace productivity increases in proportion to the societal investment. It may require a surplus economy to permit cosmetic rehabilitation for minor disfigurements. Classifying cosmetic surgery as a luxury service, denying it public funds, or ensuring that surgeons are a scarce resource to be carefully allocated would all serve to limit public access.

Currently, in the realm of rectifying deformity, control is in the hands of the medical and dental professions and their patients. Because medical treatment of this nature is now often covered by health insurance or public welfare programs, the market of potential patients has increased. What once may have been a luxury is now accessible to a wider segment of Americans. As a consequence, the medical profession can control access to cosmetic changes of a surgical nature. The willingness to perform surgery and patient selection are crucial "gate-keeper" functions for the profession, especially since physicians have the unusual capacity to develop and manage their own market.

This situation calls upon the profession to regulate itself and perform surgery only when it is absolutely necessary. Learning when surgical intervention is not necessary becomes very important, for a decision not to operate often implies normalcy. A statement from a surgeon that "this is not serious enough to operate on" is a guarantee of physical acceptability. In the case of multiple rehabilitative plastic surgical procedures, the surgeon's statement that "there is no more that I can do" permits the patient and family to adapt to limitation and residual disfigurement.

One of the dangers of placing normalization within the medical context is the propensity of well-socialized physicians to intervene whenever requested. Eagerness to perform surgery has caused a great deal of criticism of the medical profession. A study of heart transplant surgeons (Fox and Swazey, '74,) revealed how surgery can become a personal crusade in battling illness and death. Critics of the medical profession have stated that it is unfair to ask a profession to both evaluate need and provide treatment. The granting of such broad responsibility can lead to excessive amounts of surgery and "surgical fashion."

Crile ('75) discusses the surgeon's dilemma as being a conflict of interest inherent in being the judge and also having a personal stake in the results of the judgment. He points out that the surgeon " . . . is paid if he operates and not paid if he doesn't." Crile, a surgeon himself, opposes fee-for-service surgery because he believes it encourages excessive treatment.

While he finds financial gain to be a major cause for the performance of larger numbers and more extensive surgical procedures, he also finds the surgeon's activism to be a factor. He sees the surgeon's love for the art and practice of surgery as being responsible for his enthusiasm and believes that the social situation and the role of the surgeon in America defines a good deal about how he or she practices. As a case in point, Crile discusses the situation of the uncommon operation, such as a major craniofacial procedure, where the surgeon has to decide whether he or she should operate as a non-expert or refer the patient to a specialized and active center. While the center might perform the surgery better and more safely, the surgeon is tempted to develop experience in the procedure and perform it himself or herself. The role of the surgeon creates the conflict of interest here.

Bunker ('70) compared the number of operations per capita in the U.S., England and Wales and found the rate to be approximately twice as high in the U.S. He convincingly links this to the fact that the U.S. has nearly twice as many surgeons per unit population than does Great Britain. Lewis ('69) found three to four-fold variations in regional rates for six common surgical procedures in the U.S. and found that the number of surgeons available was a significant predictor.

The number of surgeons *per capita* bears strongly upon what these surgeons will define as their legitimate activities. When surgeons are scarce, they must perceive themselves as a precious resource and decide what types of procedures they will perform and who they will serve. Under conditions where surgeons exist in an adequate or surplus supply, individual surgeons have less choice regarding what they will do, and the gate-keeper function is relaxed, especially with regard to elective procedures. In the case of facial surgery, a high degree of willingness to perform surgery has its problems. Does willingness to operate raise the chances that people who would have otherwise adapted successfully to a condition seek and receive treatment?

Particular historic or economic factors can stimulate an upward spiral in a discrete area of surgery or in a special operation. For example, Fox and Swazey ('74) point out that media coverage and publicity at the outset of cardiac transplantation stimulated surgeons to undertake and continue these procedures. Their analysis of the rise and fall of the rate of heart transplant operations makes it evident that factors other than clinical success alone may determine the utilization of a surgical procedure. The clinical moratorium on heart transplants, which occurred between December 1967 and 1970, provides an excellent example of how the performance of surgery may be regulated within a community of peers.

New procedures are often accompanied by the risks of "surgical fashion" and patient disappointment, which deserve scrutiny. The study of the diffusion of medical innovations reveals patterns in the utilization and adoption of new drugs and treatment. A new treatment receiving preliminary attention in the professional literature will be employed by a small number of innovators who see themselves as research-oriented or trailblazers. Once these innovators report clinical success, a broader, less experimental group of practitioners employ the new treatment on a wider scale; the desire to "try something new" or "to be up with the times" encourages rapid and wide-spread utilization of new treatments. It is during this period of large scale utilization that the limitations of the new treatment usually become apparent and the risk of practioners being fashionable, as opposed to cautious, is at its highest. As the limitations and side-effects become increasingly evident, a generally more judicious use of the new treatment occurs, and in some cases, limitations are severe enough to warrant dooming a therapy to extinction. Hopefully, limitations become apparent before any serious harm is caused, but the process of screening innovations does not assure this in any absolute sense. The use of Thalidomide in West Germany, which caused birth defects, and radiation to the thyroid, which later induced cancer, bear testimony to the dangers of rapid innovation where side-effects become apparent only in the long run. Controls on drug innovations have become increasingly stringent and generally effective in assuring safe utilization. No such screening process is available for surgical innovations. Therefore, it becomes important that new procedures be applied with great caution and careful patient selection.

The surgical treatment of jaw deformities provides an example of a surgical innovation that became widely utilized in a fairly short time period. The dramatic increase in the use of these operations relates to historical factors as well as to the fact that they have been quite successful clinically. Indeed, only recently have the limitations of these operations become really apparent, and concerns have been expressed regarding relapse, mortality and postsurgical speech changes. Hinds and Kent ('72) say in their textbook on this subject that " . . . due in great part to the influence of Köle, Schuchardt, Trauner and Obwegeser, the larger field of maxillomandibular deformities has become widely explored during the last decade in this country, and a *whole new world* has been opened for the oral surgeon." This new world provides the opportunity to perform new types of surgery and serves as a reaffirmation of the competence of the oral surgeon/dentist within the hospital medical community.

Irby ('75), a prominent oral surgeon, discusses the "sporadic and turbulent" history of oral surgery in the United States, particularly in its relations to the medical profession. He documents a series of historical rebuffs directed at oral surgery by organized medicine, and goes on to say that " . . . the increase in numbers and organizational strength of plastic surgeons and otorhinolaryngologists has also posed a threat to the activities of the oral surgeon, for there is much interest among these groups in many procedures traditionally performed by the oral surgeon." He points to the recently increased emphasis on certain procedures as an area of specialization " . . . in which the oral surgeon is most competent and skillful, and one which he should, therefore, *pursue with vigor*." Thus, the increase in use of these maxillofacial surgical procedures is occurring in a context of interprofessional rivalries and in defense of a specialty's turf. Perhaps even more than financial considerations, threats to professional status can hinder vigilant control of how often and on whom a procedure is performed.

Patient selection becomes a particularly sensitive concern in the area of cosmetic surgery. These uniformly elective procedures possess the potential for markedly altering individual identity. People seeking such changes desire improvement and experience a rise in expectations (social, cosmetic, marital, etc.) prior to surgery. The potential for disappointment is great since even if objective cosmetic alterations are a "success", there is no guarantee that the associated social expectations will be fulfilled. Indeed, there is reason to believe that even after stigmas are no longer apparent, people often maintain identities and personalities based upon them. Guides for selecting patients (Courtiss, '78) and for understanding psychiatric problems (Meyer, '64) associated with aesthetic surgery exist and are helpful to the clinician interested in facilitating adaptation to change. Currently, the basic mode of surgical decision-making remains the same; the surgeon alone determines criteria and decides on whom he will operate. This gate-keeping mechanism is currently undergoing a challenge by insurance carriers and public agencies that fund and scrutinize health care. The use of second opinions and certificates of need point to future institutional constraints on who receives elective surgical care. Public welfare and third party interaction raises the very real questions of "when is a difference a defect?" or "when is it reasonable for a society to bear the burden of providing an operation?" Both questions imply a growing interest in determining surgical need and monitoring surgical endeavors.

The increase of interest in surgical activities from outside the medical profession may signal the beginning of controls over its activism. This interest rises from an appreciation that the public has abdicated its social responsibility to the medical profession. This appreciation comes at a time when increasing numbers of people are coming to understand the limitations on science's ability to make ethical and value-based judgments for the society. Decisions about medical and scientific activism and about social norms (including aesthetic norms) will require input from a variety of sources, including the spiritual, economic and political viewpoints, in order to assure that moral and equitable choices are made.

SUMMARY

The potential for cosmetic facial and maxillofacial surgery to alleviate human suffering is great, yet the endeavor itself has a number of inherent difficulties. Cautious and thoughtful decision-making and resource allocation are necessary to avoid the extremes of medical activism or the appeal of normalization. In the process of treating facial disfigurement, one grapples with the basic question of how a society deals with differences. Decisions about whether to integrate, to alter or to reject differences are significant and fundamental moral choices.

ACKNOWLEDGMENTS

The author wishes to thank Jeffrey Beame, Mary Carter, Justin Fink and Sue Slatkoff for their comments and assistance.

REFERENCES

Bunker, J. P. Surgical manpower: A comparison of operations and surgeons in the United States and England and Wales. N. E. J. Med. *282*:135-144, 1970.

Courtiss, E. H. (ed.) *Aesthetic Surgery — Trouble; How to Avoid It and How to Treat It*. C. V. Mosby, St. Louis, 1978.

Crile, G., Jr. *The Surgeon's Dilemma*. Harpers, 1975.

Davis, B. D. Prospects for genetic intervention in man. Sci. *170*:1282, 1970.

Fiedler, L. *Freaks, Myths and Images of the Secret Self*. Simon and Schuster, New York, 1978.

Fox, R. C. and J. P. Swazey. *The Courage to Fail — A Social View of Organ-Transplants and Dialysis*. University of Chicago Press, Chicago, 1974.

Goffman, E. *Stigma — Notes on the Management of Spoiled Identity*. Prentice-Hall, Englewood Cliffs, N.J., 1963.

Gustafson, J. M. Genetic engineering and the normative view of the human. In: *Ethical Issues in Biology and Medicine*, P. N. Williams (ed.). Schenkman, Cambridge, pp. 46-58, 1972.

Hinds, E. C. and J. N. Kent. *Surgical Treatment of Development Jaw Deformities*. C. V. Mosby, St. Louis, 1972.

Irby, W. B. History of the development of oral surgery in the United States. In: *Oral and Maxillofacial Surgery*, Vol. 1, H. W. Archer (ed.). W. B. Saunders, Philadelphia, pp. 11, 1975.

Ivy, R. C. Nazi war crimes of a medical nature. In: *Federation Bulletin*, Federation of State Medical Boards of the U. S., Inc., pp. 133-146, 1947.

Lewis, C. E. Variations in the incident of surgery. N. E. J. Med. *281*:880-884, 1969.

MacGregor, F. C. *Transformation and Identify — The Face and Plastic Surgery.* New York Times Book Co., N.Y., 1974.

Meyer, E. Psychiatric aspect of plastic surgery. In: *Reconstructive Plastic Surgery*, Vol. 1, J. M. Converse (ed.). W. B. Saunders, Philadelphia, pp. 365-383, 1964.